Wrought Iron

ITS MANUFACTURE, CHARACTERISTICS

AND APPLICATIONS

By JAMES ASTON

Consulting Metallurgist, A. M. Byers Company

and EDWARD B. STORY

Chief Metallurgist, A. M. Byers Company

SECOND EDITION · PRICE $1.00

Published by

A. M. BYERS COMPANY

Pittsburgh, Pennsylvania

PREFACE TO SECOND EDITION

DURING *the past decade there has been a rapidly growing demand for wrought iron in many different products. This demand has been accompanied by a need for information on the qualities of the material and their application to present day problems. This handbook is dedicated to that need.*

The manufacture of wrought iron is the oldest branch of the ferrous metal industry, and until recent years the details concerning the methods employed were not generally known because a high degree of individual skill was required to produce good quality material. Thus, in many cases, users of wrought iron had available very little reliable information on which to base their decisions.

This book has been written to serve as a source of up to date information on wrought iron for all who are interested in problems of material selection as well as for those students in colleges and universities who may someday become responsible for engineering specifications. In order to make the subject matter both clearly understandable and concise, no attempt has been made to go into minute details concerning the history of wrought iron manufacture, since that covers a period of several thousand years and much of it has no direct bearing on present day or future problems. For the sake of clarity, numerous photographs have been employed to better illustrate the various phases of the subject.

The wide acceptance accorded the first edition of this volume has been a source of inspiration and gratification to the authors. Many comments on the text have been received which contained helpful suggestions or criticisms. Many of these comments have formed the basis for revisions in the text of this second edition. Also, some new material has been added which it is felt will serve to enhance the value of this volume to all members of the engineering and educational professions.

Preface

The successful completion of this work has been made possible through the friendly cooperation of many individuals whose contributions, constructive criticisms, and practical suggestions are acknowledged with thanks.

J. A.
E. B. S.

Pittsburgh, Penna.
July 11, 1939

TABLE OF CONTENTS

CHAPTER I

CHAPTER II

CHAPTER III

CHAPTER IV

CHAPTER V

CHAPTER VI

CHAPTER VII

CHAPTER VIII

Contents

CHAPTER IX

Chapter I

WROUGHT IRON

WROUGHT iron is best described as a two-component metal consisting of high purity iron and iron silicate—a particular type of glass-like slag. The iron and the slag are in physical association, as contrasted to the chemical or alloy relationship that generally exists between the constituents of other metals. Wrought iron is the only ferrous metal that contains siliceous slag.

Many different processes have been employed in the manufacture of wrought iron during the thousands of years it has been made and used by man. Naturally, vast improvements have been made in manufacturing methods as well as in the quality of the finished wrought iron, but, peculiarly, the characteristics of the metal and the metallurgical principles used in producing it have remained unchanged. With any method of manufacture, the initial product, which is subsequently squeezed and rolled, is always composed of a pasty or semi-fused mass of cohering, slag-coated granules of refined iron.

Until comparatively recent times, the slag content of wrought iron was considered as an undesirable impurity. It was present because the maximum temperatures obtainable in the furnaces used were not sufficiently high to keep the iron in the molten or liquid state after the greater portion of the metalloid impurities, principally carbon, had been eliminated. In other words, during the final stages of the refining operations, the fusion temperature of the iron was equal to or above the temperature of the furnace, thus causing the refined iron to solidify and, in so doing, to entrain some of the molten siliceous slag in which it was partially immersed. Today, of course, the slag is generally recognized as being responsible in a large measure for the desirable properties

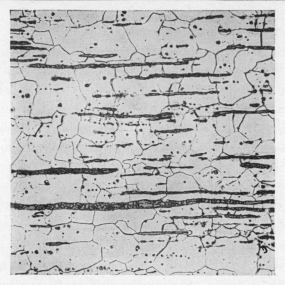

This photomicrograph of wrought iron, taken at 100 magnifications, shows clearly the glass-like siliceous slag fibres embedded in the high purity iron base metal.

of wrought iron—particularly its resistance to corrosion and to fatigue.

In 1930, the American Society for Testing Materials adopted the following definition of wrought iron that takes into account the facts stated above.

"Wrought Iron—A ferrous material, aggregated from a solidifying mass of pasty particles of highly refined metallic iron, with which, without subsequent fusion, is incorporated a minutely and uniformly distributed quantity of slag."

The iron silicate or slag content in wrought iron may vary from about 1% to 3% or more, by weight, depending upon the amount of rolling necessary to produce the finished section. It is distributed throughout the iron base metal in the form of threads or fibres which extend in the direction of rolling. In well made wrought iron, there may be 250,000 or more of these glass-like slag fibres to each cross-sectional square inch. The slag content occupies a considerably greater volume than the percentage by weight would indicate, because the specific gravity of the slag is much lower than that of the iron base metal.

The accompanying photomicrograph of wrought iron taken at 100 magnifications shows the manner in which the non-rusting slag fibres are incorporated in the highly refined base metal. The presence of these fibres gives the metal a tough, fibrous structure similar to that of hickory wood. This similarity can be seen easily by comparing pieces of each material that have been nicked and fractured slowly.

A typical chemical analysis of wrought iron showing the distribution of metalloids in the two constituents is listed as follows:

DISTRIBUTION OF CONSTITUENTS
Chemical Composition

Elements	Combined Analysis	Constituents Occurring in Base Metal	Constituents Occurring in Slag
Carbon	.02%	.02%	—
Manganese	.03	.01	.02%
Phosphorus	.12	.10	.02
Sulphur	.02	.02	—
Silicon	.15	.01	.14
Slag, by Weight	3.00	—	—
Total Metalloids		.16	.18

A clear understanding of the internal structural and chemical differences between wrought iron and other commonly used ferrous metals may be obtained by comparing this photomicrograph and analysis with those in Chapter V.

Chapter II

WROUGHT IRON MANUFACTURE
PRIOR TO 1850

WROUGHT iron was known and used long before the beginnings of recorded history and evidences of this are available today. In the Bible, Genesis, IV, 22, mention is made of iron cutting instruments. A wrought iron sickle blade was found beneath the base of a sphinx in Karnak, near Thebes, Egypt, while a blade probably 5000 years old was found in one of the pyramids. Numerous other similar discoveries have been made in Europe, the Mediterranean countries and the Far East.

All of the early methods used for wrought iron manufacture were based on producing the finished product in one operation. These were known as direct methods. It was only after the introduction of the blast furnace during the fourteenth century A.D. that the indirect methods were developed.

PRIMITIVE METHODS

Man's first acquaintance with wrought iron probably was the result of an accident caused by the building of a fire in a locality where the earth was rich in iron ore. Little or nothing is known about the primitive developments, but undoubtedly the use of iron began when it was found that this material could be forged readily into weapons tougher and stronger than wood or stone.

The production of wrought iron became a matter of great importance to our primitive ancestors, and in the course of time they learned to distinguish the iron-bearing ore that would produce the largest yield of metal and to build it into piles around their fires. Very likely they later found that the metal could be

4

produced more quickly when the ore was broken up and mixed with the fuel. The first iron furnace on which there is any information consisted merely of a hole in the ground with an opening at the bottom to provide natural draft.

Primitive Method

EARLY EGYPTIAN METHODS

The origin of forced draft in wrought iron making is unknown, but prior to about 1500 B.C. the Egyptians had developed a bellows made of goat skins with a bamboo nozzle and an air inlet valve. The operator of the bellows, probably a slave, stood on the skin bag to expel the air and reinflated it by pulling up on a string attached to the top. The use of forced draft was one of the first major developments in wrought iron manufacture.

While the Egyptians' furnaces were crude, consisting merely of pits into which the ore and fuel were placed, the enduring qualities of the wrought iron produced in them is indicated by the excellent condition of implements and other equipment found when exploring ancient tombs.

Early Egyptian Method

ASIATIC IMPROVEMENTS

The development of the original furnace, as such, is generally credited to the Asiatics, who also introduced the idea of adding layers of the ore and fuel mixture at the top of the fire as reduction took place. The early Asiatic

Asiatic Method

furnace had a trough at the top from which the smelter raked the raw materials on the fire.

Bellows of improved design were used to supply the forced draft. In operating them, the heel of the worker's bare foot on the downward stroke closed small holes in the top, thus forcing air into the furnace. On the upward stroke, the top of the bellows being raised by means of a string attached to a springy rod, the holes were uncovered permitting reinflation.

As reduction took place, the refined iron collected at the bottom of the furnace in a spongy mass which, after a sufficient amount had been obtained, was taken out and forged.

DEVELOPMENT OF FURNACES USED IN THE DIRECT PROCESSES

There were many variations in design of the early furnaces used for wrought iron production in different parts of the world. However, many furnaces were of the "shaft" type while others were of the so-called "hearth" type.

About the eighth century A.D. a new furnace known as the Osmund furnace was developed and used extensively. It was square in cross section, somewhat larger at the top than at the bottom, and approximately ten feet high. There were numerous modifications of this furnace. Later designs were circular in

13th Century Improvement—Catalan Forge

6

cross section, with the point of greatest diameter occurring a few feet above the bottom. Forced draft was supplied by means of bellows. As far as it is known, shaft furnaces were used mainly in India and Sweden. The upper portion of the shaft was used both as a stack and as an opening for charging the fuel and iron ore. When the iron was refined and had collected on the bottom in a spongy mass, an opening would be made in one side of the furnace to permit removal of the "ball."

The Catalan Forge, originated about 1293 A.D. by the iron workers of Catalonia in Spain, represented a major advance in the manufacture of wrought iron direct from the ore. This was a hearth type furnace consisting of a hearth or crucible in which the mixture of ore and fuel was placed. The air-blast, produced by means of a trompe or water blower, entered the furnace through tuyeres near the bottom.

The efficiency of the Catalan Forge, which is said to have produced about 140 pounds of wrought iron in five hours, was considerably higher than that of earlier furnaces. This furnace was introduced into the American colonies and used principally in the South.

The American Bloomery, an offspring of the Catalan Forge, represented the highest development of the hearth type of furnace. The hearth was rectangular in shape, with water cooled metal sides, and was surmounted by a chimney for carrying off the waste gases. A forced hot-blast was used, and the bellows supplying the blast were driven by a water wheel or a steam engine. As in all of the other direct processes, charcoal was used as fuel.

The Bloomery was used in this country as late as 1901 and in that connection the following comment appeared in the 1908 Annual Statistical Report of the American Iron & Steel Association, page 78:

"No forges for the manufacture of blooms and billets direct from iron ore have been in operation in the United States since 1901, in which year the blooms and billets so made amountd to 2310 gross tons, against 4292 tons in 1900 and 3142 tons in 1899. All the

Catalan forges in the South have been abandoned; so have those in the North and West."

Obviously, during the many centuries that the direct processes were used exclusively, it is to be assumed that numerous different types of equipment would have been developed. Space limitations make it impossible to mention all of the furnaces of which there is some record, and, therefore, reference has been made only to the more prominent types.

Although the direct processes for wrought iron production have been abandoned almost completely by the most advanced nations, they are still used in some parts of the world.

DOUBLE-STAGE REFINING

In the fourteenth century the wasteful and tedious method of producing wrought iron direct from the ore began to be replaced by a division of the operation into two stages. Previous to this, the single-stage reduction had been uncertain as to results and tremendously wasteful of time and materials.

Little difficulty was encountered in ridding the manganese, sulphur, phosphorus and other impurities from the iron, but the elimination of the carbon in the iron was a doubtful process, because the charcoal used as fuel was an energetic carburizing agent, and it was only by the most painstaking care that the wrought iron, when brought into contact with this fuel, was prevented from recarburizing to the point where it was no longer malleable and ductile.

It was discovered that a second heating would serve to further refine the metal which had been so over-carburized, and the wrought iron produced by this additional working was more uniform and otherwise superior to the product of the single reduction. In this second operation, which ordinarily was carried out in a Catalan type of furnace, the iron was further refined and, in addition, a portion of the slag was removed. This double-refined ball of wrought iron was called the "blume," or flower, from which the present use of the word "bloom" is derived.

8

THE DEVELOPMENT OF CAST IRON

Until the iron makers of Central Europe developed a new type of furnace around 1350, wrought iron had been the only product made from iron ore. This development was the result of efforts to reduce the fuel consumption and the cost of manufacture by increasing the size, and especially the height, of the furnaces used in the production of wrought iron. However, the product of this new furnace was not wrought iron since it was taken from the furnace in the molten state, as contrasted to the slag-impregnated sponge-like mass of iron secured from the furnaces or forges in which wrought iron was made. Also, upon cooling, this new metal possessed properties unlike those of wrought iron in that it was hard and brittle, and, when fractured exhibited a crystalline or granular structure as contrasted to the tough, fibrous structure of wrought iron.

This new furnace, known as a "stuckofen," was the progenitor of the modern blast furnace, and, like all furnaces of that time, it required the use of charcoal as fuel. The raw materials—iron ore, flux and charcoal—were charged in at the top of this furnace, while air, under very low pressure was blown in at the bottom.

Coke was first considered as a fuel in 1619, but it did not come into extensive use until about 1730 when Darby successfully applied it to blast furnace operation. This development was followed by the introduction of the hot blast in the early 1800's. The greatest improvements in blast furnace design and operation have been made since 1880.

While the product of the stuckofen, or blast furnace, was not malleable and ductile, and could not be hammered or forged and welded like wrought iron, it was soon discovered that the new metal could be cast into various useful shapes. Thus, cast iron was introduced. Subsequently, the principal product of the blast furnace became known as "pig iron" because it was cast in small moulds or "pigs." In this form it is remelted and used for the manufacture of other products.

9

THE DEVELOPMENT OF CHARCOAL IRON

Shortly after the commercial production of pig iron was commenced, the need for a more highly refined material than cast iron led to the introduction of so-called charcoal iron. Originally, charcoal iron—also called knobbled iron—was made by charging alternate layers of pig metal and charcoal upon the hearth of a small rectangular furnace provided with a stack and a number of tuyeres for the introduction of cold air blast. The temperature in this furnace became sufficiently high to melt and partially purify the pig iron. Most of the silicon and some of the phosphorus was eliminated. This partially purified metal, when tapped out, was allowed to solidify and was then broken up and charged into a second furnace with alternate layers of charcoal. As the metal was melted in this second furnace, it was further purified and practically all the carbon removed. Since it was impossible to obtain high temperatures in this furnace, the molten metal, as it trickled down through the mass of iron and charcoal, became partially solidified by the time it reached the furnace bottom and in this stage entrained a small amount of the refining slag. The spongy mass of iron and the entrained slag in the bottom of the furnace was collected from time to time and pressed into a bloom.

Charcoal iron, as made by this process, differs from wrought iron in that it has a higher carbon content and a considerably lower slag content. Furthermore, the slag consists almost entirely of iron oxide in charcoal iron, while the slag entrained in wrought iron is of a glass-like siliceous type which is considered much more resistant to corrosion than the iron oxide type slag.

Charcoal iron, because of its small slag content, around one per cent, possesses somewhat more ductility than does genuine wrought iron. This higher degree of ductility is most pronounced opposite to the fibre direction. Accordingly it has found some use for applications where severe fabrication must be withstood. At present this material is used very little except for boiler tubes which must be expanded and beaded into crown sheets.

It may be well to remark that charcoal iron as manufactured today, is not the same material as that of days gone by. In making this type of material today, pig iron is rarely used, but in its stead, light steel scrap, generally of the low carbon variety, is employed.

INDIRECT PROCESSES—THE PUDDLING PROCESS

The production of pig iron led to the development of the indirect processes for the manufacture of wrought iron. Unfortunately, little is known about the early attempts to produce wrought iron from pig iron rather than direct from the ore, but it is believed that the first ones were made in Belgium using a hearth type furnace. The reverberatory furnace was invented about 1613 but it was not used for refining pig iron until 1766.

In 1784, Henry Cort, an Englishman, utilized the reverberatory furnace in the development of his revolutionary "Dry Puddling" process for wrought iron manufacture. He hollowed out the hearth of the furnace so as to make a "puddle" of molten iron which was stirred to speed up the refining operation. The hearth was lined with sand which fused with some of the iron oxide resulting from partial oxidation of the iron to form a siliceous slag. Coal instead of charcoal was used as fuel. Following is Cort's own description of his furnace:

> "For the preparing, manufacturing, and working of iron from the ore, as well as from sow and pig metal, and also from every other sort of cast iron, I make use of a reverberatory or air furnace, the bottoms of which are laid hollow or dished out, so as to contain the metal when in a fluid state."

In this furnace the hot gases from the burning coal passed over and fused the charge of iron thus removing most of the metalloid impurities by oxidation. Unfortunately, Cort's "Dry Puddling" process was very wasteful of iron and in some instances the iron loss amounted to as much as 30% of the total metal charged.

Several years later, about 1830, Joseph Hall modified Cort's development in an effort to reduce the iron loss. He substituted

11

old bottom material for the sand hearth lining and thus introduced the oxide bottom which cut the iron loss to about 10%, shortened the time of the heat, and made possible the use of almost all grades of pig iron.

This new process was first called "Wet Puddling" due to the large amount of slag formed. It was also known as the "Pigboiling Process" because of the vigorous boiling of the molten metal during the refining operation. Today this process is referred to generally as the "Puddling Process."

The most important fact about the puddling process was that the production of wrought iron was increased greatly, growing in one plant from ten tons per week by the old methods to two hundred tons per week with the new. Also, the handling of larger masses of iron and the use of improved methods and equipment made available a wrought iron of better quality than that produced previously.

Naturally, minor improvements were made from time to time but essentially the puddling process as used in this country conformed to Cort's and Hall's original developments of more than a century ago. The furnace commonly used was a simple, coal-fired reverberatory, sometimes having a waste heat boiler in the stack. In the Pittsburgh district the single furnace, manned by two puddlers and charged with about 600 pounds of pig iron, was generally employed. A typical installation is illustrated by the photographs on page 14. In the East double furnaces were the rule. Essentially these consisted of two single furnaces back to back, with the back walls removed to make a single hearth. Four puddlers, two on each side, were required to work the charge.

18th Century Development—The Puddling Furnace

The hearth on which the iron was worked in the puddling furnace of either type had a cinder (iron oxide) bottom lined with plastic iron ore. The cold pig iron charged was refined to the desired wrought iron in about 1¾ hours. The heat cycle comprised several steps. First, the pig iron was melted. Then iron oxide in the form of roll scale was added to the bath of molten metal, which was thoroughly agitated by the puddler using a "rabble." The oxidizing reaction, coupled with the basic conditions maintained by the furnace lining, effected an almost complete elimination of the carbon, silicon, sulphur, phosphorus, and manganese originally present in the pig iron, the composition of the refined metal approaching that of virtually pure iron.

The slag produced during the refining reactions was an iron silicate, high in iron oxide ratio. As refining progressed, the fusion temperature of the metal bath increased due to the reduction in the quantity of metalloids present, until at the approach to completion of the heat, the furnace temperature of about 2600° F. was insufficient to maintain the metal in a liquid state. However, this temperature was high enough to keep the slag in a molten condition throughout the heat. The finishing operations, therefore, were carried out with the refined metal in a solidified or pasty condition. Under the combined influences of the reactions involved and the working by the puddler, the metal became a spongy, plastic mass impregnated with the liquid slag in which it was immersed.

Upon completion of the refining operation, the sponge-like mass of iron saturated with slag was divided in the furnace into two or three portions weighing 200 to 300 pounds each and formed into coherent balls which, at a welding heat, were taken from the furnace and put through a squeezer. The squeezer or press ejected the surplus slag and formed the metal into compact blooms which were immediately rolled into rough, flat sections called "muck bar." The muck bar was then sheared to short lengths which were piled, reheated to a welding temperature, and rolled to the desired shapes.

13

The 200-300 pound Sponge Ball Produced in the Puddling Furnace

The "piling" operation was desirable to obtain a more uniform finished material and to provide a mass of metal sufficiently large to work properly. No two puddlers could produce material chemically and physically the same, so, for uniformity's sake, muck bar from a number of different furnaces was used to make up the "pile." With the present-day methods described in one of the following chapters, the piling operation, strictly speaking, is unnecessary because much larger masses of iron are handled with accurate, scientific control to supersede the skill of the puddler.

The hand-puddling operation, like all other methods used in the manufacture of quality wrought iron, produced a coherent, sponge-like mass of highly refined metallic iron in which was incorporated a quantity of siliceous slag. The "sponge-ball," as it is commonly termed, consists of many thousands of small slag-coated particles of refined iron which are welded together to form the finished material.

14

Chapter III

MODERN DEVELOPMENTS AND RESEARCH IN WROUGHT IRON MANUFACTURE

FROM the time it was introduced until within the past decade, the hand-puddling process was the principal means used to supply the world's requirements for wrought iron. However, the hand-puddling process had serious limitations, particularly from the standpoint of quantity production and physical uniformity of the finished product. As a result, numerous attempts were made to develop machines that would do the same work that the puddler did in operating a hand-puddling furnace. As a matter of historical interest, several of the more prominent efforts are mentioned briefly as follows.

MECHANICAL PUDDLING FURNACES

One of the first of the mechanically operated furnaces was known as the Danks Puddling Furnace, which was used to some extent in this country between the years 1868 and 1885. This furnace was cylindrical in shape, and in order to agitate the metal charge, was rotated about a horizontal axis. While this furnace embodied most of the features of some of the more successful efforts of later date, it was a failure for several reasons, including the absence of suitable refractory materials, a lack of knowledge and facilities for control and study of products, and non-uniformity of product.

The Roe Puddling Furnace, invented about 1905 by James P. Roe, was used by Reading Iron Company, Reading, Pennsylvania, for a part of their production from about 1920 until that company went out of business in 1938. The furnace proper was rectangular in shape, 12 feet wide and 24 feet long, with a trough-like bottom.

In order to agitate the charge, the furnace could be oscillated through various angles up to 120 degrees. The charge consisted of 3 tons or more of molten pig iron from a blast furnace together with fluid puddling cinder melted in an open-hearth furnace. Gas was used as fuel and the refining reactions paralleled those of hand-puddling, with each heat requiring about one hour for completion.

The Ford Process was the invention of E. L. Ford of Youngstown, Ohio. It was operated experimentally for a number of years before being placed on a commercial basis during the early 1920's. This mechanical furnace was similar to a Bessemer Converter in size and shape and rotated about a horizontal axis. The working of each heat of about 2000 pounds required about one-half hour. The process was operated intermittently for several years but production was not of a commercial order.

The Ely Process of mechanical puddling, patented by W. C. Ely of Terre Haute, Indiana, and later purchased by the American Chain Company, Inc., was originally intended solely for busheling scrap iron mechanically. It was operated successfully for several years for that purpose before it was adapted for the puddling of pig iron about 1921. The furnace itself was about 5 feet square in cross section and 6 feet in axial length. This box-like structure was supported on two large carrier rings which were mounted on power-driven rolls. This arrangement permitted the furnace to be rotated or oscillated as required. Each heat, with a charge of 750 to 800 pounds of molten pig iron, required about 35 minutes for completion.

Another interesting mechanical puddling development was the Hibbard furnace invented by H. D. Hibbard of Plainfield, New Jersey. This furnace, first operated on a commercial basis in 1921, was essentially of the rotating-barrel type, somewhat similar in construction to the older Danks furnace. The maximum capacity of the furnace was about 1500 pounds of molten pig iron which was worked into the finished product in a little more than 45 minutes.

The foregoing brief descriptions cover the dominant efforts in this country along the lines of mechanical puddling. There were numerous other attempts which quite generally were without merit and most of them did not advance beyond the paper stage.

It will be observed that all of the processes described were planned to follow the general lines of hand-puddling, by effecting refining, disintegration and balling of the metal in one furnace. Rotary or oscillatory movement of the furnace was substituted for the manual effort of the puddler without taking into consideration the important fact, which was discovered subsequently through research, that the quality of the wrought iron produced in the hand-puddling furnace was directly proportional to the skill of the puddler and beyond that skill no scientific control was possible. Thus, the primary obstacle to successful mechanical puddling was a lack of control and of consistency of product, as related to different heats or throughout the mass of a single heat

RESEARCH ON WROUGHT IRON

The failure or only partial success of the various mechanical puddling furnaces led to an entirely new but most logical approach to the problem of wrought iron manufacture. This method of approach was just as radical a departure from the accepted principles as was Cort's development of 1784. It involved a study of the metal itself by utilizing to the fullest extent the modern metallurgical microscope and the chemical laboratory.

Prior to 1915 practically all the attention had been given to the methods for producing wrought iron with very little effort directed toward a study of the metal itself. In fact, wrought iron was believed to consist of "thousands of fibres of pure iron, each coated with an oxidized slag and each welded firmly to the other fibres." This belief still persists in some rare instances at the present time.

However, in 1915 an exhaustive study of the metal—wrought iron—was started. Hundreds of samples of old wrought irons, with known records of service, were analyzed in the chemical laboratory and studied under the microscope. It was found that the metal consisted of a matrix of high purity iron in which thousands of threads or fibres of ferrous silicate were embedded. The microscope revealed that approximately 250,000 of the siliceous fibres were present in each cross-sectional square inch of good quality wrought iron.

Also, it was found that the wrought irons, as produced by hand methods, showed many startling variations in chemical composition. In the light of known records on the many specimens under observation, this total lack of uniformity with respect to chemical constituents led to the obvious conclusion that these variations had no practical effect on the durability of wrought iron subjected to corrosive conditions, provided the material consistently retained those two fundamental characteristics—purity of the base metal and the embedded ferrous silicate fibres—which distinguish it from other metals.

This study of old samples of wrought irons which have definitely established their durability under actual service conditions has been continued during the intervening years. As a matter of interest, analyses and abbreviated service data on more than fifty specimens of the material are given in Tables I, II, III, and IV. These analyses have been separated into four main groups which are listed as follows:

Table   I.   Wrought irons containing normal phosphorus and no copper.

Table   II.   Wrought irons containing normal phosphorus and varying amounts of copper.

Table III.   Wrought irons containing high phosphorus and no copper.

Table IV.   Wrought irons containing high phosphorus and varying amounts of copper.

In studying the tables of analyses it should be kept in mind that during the period when these wrought irons were produced, knowledge of chemistry and metallurgy was very meager. Little was known of the chemical composition of ores, and the product of their reduction—pig iron—was classified according to fracture. It happened that some of the ores used in the manufacture of wrought iron contained high phosphorus and others low phosphorus; some had traces of copper while others contained no copper. So, by chance, the wrought iron, depending upon the ore supply, showed variations in phosphorus and copper contents. It will be observed that these variations were by no means uniform and in most cases the copper content was so small that it had no effect on the properties of the material. The content of other metalloid constituents varied also, but lack of scientific control was responsible since they could be reduced by oxidation in the refining operations.

The results of this research on the structural characteristics and chemical composition of good quality wrought iron formed the basis for the development of the present-day manufacturing process which is described in the following chapter.

TABLE I.

Analyses of Wrought Irons Containing Normal Phosphorus and No Copper

C	Mn	P	S	Si	Slag	Cu.	Placed in Service	Removed from Service	Age	Remarks
.023	.026	.163	.023	.122	3.35		1895		41	16″ pipe line owned by the Pittsburgh & West Virginia Gas Co., located between Central, W. Va., and Littleton, W. Va. The operating pressure of this line varies from 140 to 200 pounds per square inch.
.028	.070	.180	.022	.212	2.68		About 1860	1929	69	Wrought iron rail chair found buried in wet clay soil along Central of Georgia Rwy. tracks about 40 miles east of Macon, Ga. This type rail chair has been obsolete since the Civil War.
.044	.059	.157	.014	.235	3.23		1892		44	4″ wrought iron pipe (sample No. 1) taken from the lines between Titusville, Pa., and Marcus Hook, Pa. laid by the U. S. Pipe Line Co. In 1923 the old pipe was sold to various other companies and reinstalled.
.030	.063	.146	.032	.202	6.22		About 1894	1934	40	1¼″ pipe taken from the original heating system in the Central Station Bldg., Chicago. Pipe had been in continuous service.
.042	.015	.181	.010	.030	1.36		About 1825	1933	108	Chain link taken from an old chain suspension bridge across the Lehigh River below Lehigh Gap, Pa. Wrought iron link still in good condition. Sample No. 1.
.038	.033	.180	.034	.197	3.97		1888	1934	46	16″ suction line used in drydock No. 1 at the Philadelphia Navy Yard.
.020	.022	.172	.020	.169	3.98		1881		55	Wrought iron plate from locomotive watering tank owned by A. T. & S. F. R. R. at National City, California.
.036	.022	.152	.020	.160	2.93		1884	1931	47	⅜″ plate taken from the open spill tanks serving the hydraulic elevators in the old Home Insurance Bldg., Chicago, which was razed in 1931.
.019	.141	.145	.025	.178	3.16		1894	1934	40	1¼″ pipe used as underground gas service lines by the Public Service Co. of Indiana at Tipton, Indiana.

TABLE I. (CONTINUED)

Analyses of Wrought Irons Containing Normal Phosphorus and No Copper

C	Mn	P	S	Si	Slag	Cu.	Placed in Service	Removed from Service	Age	Remarks
.050	.026	.170	.025	.150	3.32		1884	1928	44	8″ pipe fabricated from No. 14 gauge wrought iron sheets used as underground water line and owned by the Water Dept., City of Santa Cruz, California.
.056	.030	.152	.025	.150	2.80		1899		37	14″ pipe fabricated from 9 & 11 gauge wrought iron sheets, still in service as underground water supply line. This line, when last examined, was operated by the Water Dept. of the City of Santa Cruz, Calif., at 225 pounds pressure.
.020	.019	.192	.028	.280	3.87		1876	1935	59	¾″ round wrought iron bar taken from the railing on the old Mill Creek Bridge at Clifton Ave. in Cincinnati. Bridge was replaced in 1935.
.046	.056	.187	.025	.197	2.98		1904	1932	28	¾″ pipe sample from the sprinkler line in McCreery's Department Store, Pgh., Pa. Pipe still in excellent condition.
.012	.026	.148	.025	.139	4.00		About 1887	1926	39	6⅝″ casing taken from Well No. 28 drilled by the Phila. Co. on the Verner Farm in Westmoreland Co., Pa. In good condition when removed.

TABLE II.

Analyses of Wrought Irons Containing Normal Phosphorus and Varying Amounts of Copper

C	Mn	P	S	Si	Slag	Cu.	Placed in Service	Removed from Service	Age	Remarks
.026	.033	.158	.025	.329	4.30	.176	1870		66	Wrought iron sheet, 20 gauge, from roof of Dollar Savings Bank, Pittsburgh, Pa.
.040	.026	.138	.020	.150	2.60	.170	1877		59	Wrought iron plate originally used for a smokestack by Puget Mill Co. In 1925 the old stack was reclaimed and put in service as a penstock in the plant water supply system.
.038	.019	.151	.029	.235	3.77	.890	1864	1931	67	Cut nails taken from old Painter residence, 1027 Western Ave., Pgh., when it was razed in 1931.
.034	.030	.126	.022	.165	4.50	.080	1886	1931	45	3" x 1" tension member taken from Norfolk & Western Rwy. Bridge No. 1509 when it was replaced with a larger structure in 1931.
.038	.030	.181	.023	.188	3.41	.130	1886	1931	45	Section No. 1 of Phoenix Column taken from Norfolk & Western Rwy. Bridge No. 1509.
.020	.026	.180	.023	.188	3.69	.120	1886	1931	45	Section No. 2 of Phoenix Column taken from Norfolk & Western Rwy. Bridge No. 1509.
.036	.026	.159	.019	.141	3.76	.120	1886	1931	45	Section No. 3 of Phoenix Column taken from Norfolk & Western Rwy. Bridge No. 1509.
.032	.030	.139	.018	.132	3.98	.120	1886	1931	45	Section No. 4 of Phoenix Column taken from Norfolk & Western Rwy. Bridge No. 1509.
.026	.044	.148	.014	.194	3.37	.051	1892		44	4" pipe (Sample No. 2) taken from original oil lines laid by U. S. Pipe Line Co. between Titusville, Pa., and Marcus Hook, Penna.
.030	.019	.199	.021	.197	4.39	.140	1886		50	Rivet from wrought iron stand-pipe used in the water supply system at Vincennes, Indiana.
.037	.041	.081	.018	.056	2.31	.110	1906	1933	27	Wrought iron plate taken from hull of U. S. Engineer's Dredge "B. M. Harrod."

TABLE III.

Analyses of Wrought Irons Containing High Phosphorus and No Copper

C	Mn	P	S	Si	Slag	Cu.	Placed in Service	Removed from Service	Age	Remarks
.046	.037	.259	.017	.188	3.27		1889		47	Sample of 2″ pipe from cooling coils in service at Plant No. 1 of the Merchant's Ice & Cold Storage Co., Louisville, Ky.
.047	.041	.235	.029	.165	4.36		1885	1931	46	Sample of plate from smokestack at old Etna Furnace, Etna, Tenn. Stack to be re-erected at the Protestant Hospital, Nashville, Tenn. Stack originally 256′ high.
.044	.052	.302	.024	.150	4.69		1892		44	Sample of 2″ pipe from ammonia coils in brine tank at plant of Pgh. Brewing Co., Pittsburgh, Pa. Coils still in service.
.032	.063	.370	.018	.254	3.68		1865		71	Sample of hull plating from the tugboat "Margaret" owned by the Cottman Company, Baltimore, Md. One hull plate replaced in 1994; otherwise hull in good condition.
.035	.037	.373	.057	.212	4.06		1890	1934	44	Sample from 72″ diameter wrought iron water intake line in the Detroit River. Taken out of service by City of Detroit.
.053	.030	.235	.023	.212	4.94		1882	1934	52	Sample of the 8″ water line that supplied water to City of Longmont, Colo. Right-of-way change necessitated taking pipe out of service.
.040	.067	.319	.032	.197	3.58		1874	1931	57	3″ x ⅜″ wrought iron bar taken from the old Tyngsborough Bridge over the Merrimack River above Lowell, Mass.
.008	.027	.273	.017	.165	4.10		About 1825	1933	108	Chain link from an old chain suspension bridge across the Lehigh River below Lehigh Gap, Pa. Link still in good condition. Sample No. 2.
.041	.067	.266	.031	.320	3.51		1899	1934	35	4″ pipe used as a gas main at Nelsonville, Ohio, by the Ohio Fuel Gas Co.
.032	.059	.370	.028	.150	3.02		1856		80	Sample of wrought iron strap taken from the Bidwell Bar Bridge over Feather River 9.5 miles east of Oroville, Calif.

23

TABLE III. (CONTINUED)

Analyses of Wrought Irons Containing High Phosphorus and No Copper

C	Mn	P	S	Si	Slag	Cu.	Placed in Service	Removed from Service	Age	Remarks
.032	.022	.216	.027	.155	2.92		About 1870	1932	62	5″ x ½″ bar removed from elevated railway structure in New York City. Good condition.
.041	.033	.223	.023	.300	3.70		1876-80		56	Sample of 50″ O.D. water line owned by the City of Pittsburgh, Pa., and extending between Brilliant Pumping Station and Highland Reservoir No. 1.
.025	.044	.248	.021	.222	4.62		About 1885	1935	50	Sample of 6″ pipe used as a cold water line in the Grand Central Station, Chicago, Ill. Old line replaced with wrought iron pipe in January, 1936.
.007	.052	.283	.045	.144	3.18		1882		54	Sample of plate taken from hull of the sailing vessel "Joseph Conrad." This plate was fractured when vessel went aground off New York in 1935. Balance of wrought iron hull in good condition.
.022	.019	.229	.033	.188	3.90		1886		50	¼″ wrought iron plate sample taken from old water stand pipe owned by the Paducah Kentucky Water Works.
.016	.011	.270	.048	.255	3.61		1898		38	Sample of 1¼″ pipe from brine coils in service at the Topeka, Kansas, plant of John Morrell and Co.

TABLE IV.

Analyses of Wrought Irons Containing High Phosphorus and Varying Amounts of Copper

C	Mn	P	S	Si	Slag	Cu.	Placed in Service	Removed from Service	Age	Remarks
.036	.033	.257	.045	.188	3.64	.130	1881	1931	50	10" wrought iron channel taken from the old Randolph Street Viaduct in Chicago when it was dismantled in 1931.
.030	.030	.245	.023	.160	3.38	.054	1893		43	5" pipe (sample No. 3) taken from the original Oil Lines laid by the U. S. Pipe Line Co. between Titusville, Pa., and Marcus Hook, Pa.
.023	.030	.257	.023	.188	3.42	.229	1880	1932	52	Plate from the gate of old Lock No. 5 in the Great Kanawha River below Charleston, W. Va.
.024	.019	.259	.031	.178	3.94	.067	1874	1931	57	6" x ½" wrought iron bar taken from the old Tyngsborough Bridge over the Merrimack River above Lowell, Mass.
.036	.044	.240	.030	.107	1.37	.040	1910	1931	21	2" pipe from atmospheric ammonia condenser at the plant of Abbott Packing Co., Carnegie, Pa. Pipe was still in good condition and was used for other services.
.035	.070	.253	.028	.212	5.30	.090	1905		31	Sample of 4" pipe from cold water line in the U. S. Post Office, Cincinnati, Ohio. Line runs from house pump in basement to tank on fifth floor.
.036	.067	.272	.015	.141	4.03	.140	1893	1932	39	Plate from top ring of water standpipe at Provincetown, Mass.
.036	.019	.221	.018	.197	3.71	.048	1873		63	Wrought iron rod from old Highway Bridge at Havre de Grace, Maryland.
.036	.037	.230	.024	.160	3.89	.150	1893	1932	39	1¼" pipe taken from an underground water line at the Binghampton State Hospital, Binghampton, New York.
.020	.041	.479	.029	.207	4.20	.096	1884	1931	47	Pipe pile from Fort Mason Dock No. 4 in San Francisco Bay. All of the 8" wrought iron pipe piles were reinstalled in other services.
.024	.035	.284	.021	.235	3.57	.237	1873		63	3/16" plate from 36" wrought iron water conduit No. 1 owned by the City of Rochester, New York.

25

TABLE IV. (CONTINUED)

Analyses of Wrought Irons Containing High Phosphorus and Varying Amounts of Copper

C	Mn	P	S	Si	Slag	Cu.	Placed in Service	Removed from Service	Age	Remarks
.027	.019	.308	.023	.249	3.32	.290	About 1870	1922	52	3¼″ well casing used by the National Transit Co., Bear Creek Station, Parkers Landing, Pa.
.042	.011	.238	.023	.181	2.58	.130	Prior 1876	1922	46	Sample 3″ pipe from the oldest 3″ line laid in this country. The line was owned by the National Transit Co. and extended between Oil City, Pa., and Turkey City, Pa.
.028	.019	.221	.011	.122	2.42	.020	1886	1922	36	Sample of 6″ pipe from the No. 1 Karns line owned by the National Transit Co., Parkers Landing, Pa.

Chapter IV

THE PRESENT-DAY METHOD FOR
MANUFACTURING WROUGHT IRON

THE research program described briefly in the latter part of the preceding chapter probably was the first effort made to study wrought iron from the standpoint of the material itself rather than the method of manufacture. The manufacture of wrought iron, viewed from this new angle, finally resolved itself into the problem of selecting equipment suitable for carrying out each of the operations separately and subsequently combining the products of the various steps to produce the finished material.

It has been pointed out that the union or combination of the metal and the slag to produce finished wrought iron has been accomplished by various different methods. In the puddling process, for instance, the puddler, by laborious handwork, mixed the metal and the slag, with the result that the combined efforts of a puddler and his helper in a ten-hour turn yielded only about 2800 pounds of finished wrought iron. Obviously, the output of wrought iron was definitely limited by two factors: namely, the amount of equipment in use, and the number of skilled men that could be employed to operate it.

A study of the puddling process revealed that certain essential reactions took place in the puddling furnace. These are listed as follows:

1. To melt and refine the base metal.
2. To produce and keep molten a proper slag.
3. To granulate, or disintegrate, the base metal and mechanically incorporate with it the desired amount of slag.

Cupolas for Melting Pig Iron at the Ambridge, Pa., Plant of A. M. Byers Company

Bessemer Converters Are Employed to Refine the Molten Iron at the A. M. Byers Company Plant.

Siliceous Slag of an Exact Composition Is Produced in Tilting Open Hearth Furnaces.

*The Key Operation in the Production of Fine Wrought Iron at the A. M. Byers Company
Plant—Pouring the Molten Refined Iron into the Liquid Slag.*

What is now known as the Byers Process for manufacturing wrought iron conforms to the hand-puddling process in all of these three essential steps. Each step, however, is separated and carried out in individual pieces of equipment best suited to that operation. The process was placed on a commercial basis October 8, 1930, when the largest wrought iron mill in existence was formally dedicated at Ambridge, Pennsylvania. The process has resulted in a magnitude of production, control of operations, and assurance of uniformity of product undreamed of by the old iron masters.

The raw material from which wrought iron is made consists of pig iron, iron oxide, and silica. The pig iron is melted continuously in cupolas, tapped into ladles where it receives a special desulphurizing treatment, and is then conveyed to a Bessemer Converter, where it is purified to the highly refined state required

31

for the base metal in quality wrought iron. It is then carried by crane and ladle car to the processing platform and poured into the ladle of the processing machine.

In the meantime, an exact iron silicate slag formed by melting together iron oxide and certain siliceous materials in an open-hearth furnace is poured into a ladle, which is placed on a ladle car so that it can be moved to the different stations representing stages in the process. The first station is directly below the processing machine.

Next follows the key operation of the process—that of refined metal disintegration and slag incorporation. The molten refined iron is poured at a predetermined rate into the ladle containing the molten slag. The processing machine automatically oscillates as well as moves forward and backward, insuring a uniform distribution of the refined metal into the slag.

The Excess Slag Is Poured from the Ladle, Leaving the White Hot Sponge Ball of Wrought Iron.

32

Dumping the 6000-8000 pound Sponge Ball on the Platform of the 900 ton Press which Squeezes It into a Bloom.

33

Since the temperature of the slag is maintained a few hundred degrees lower than the "freezing point" of the refined iron, the latter is continuously and rapidly solidified. This rapid solidification liberates the gases dissolved in the molten metal with such force that the metal is shattered into small fragments which settle to the bottom of the slag ladle. Due to the welding temperature and the fluxing action of the siliceous slag, these fragments cohere to form a sponge-like ball of iron impregnated with the liquid slag.

Immediately upon completion of the pour, the ladle is transferred over a circular track to the next station, picked up by a crane and the surplus slag poured off into an adjoining ladle. The ladle now containing the slag is moved around the track to the open hearth station where the slag is replenished. The ladle is then moved again into position under the processing machine to start another cycle.

Meanwhile, the sponge balls weighing 6000 to 8000 pounds are dumped, one every five minutes, on the platform of a 900-ton electrically driven press. The press ejects the surplus slag and welds the cellular mass of slag-coated particles of plastic iron into a solid bloom.

The bloom of wrought iron formed during the pressing operation is rolled on the blooming mill to produce slabs or billets which are subsequently rolled on the skelp, plate, sheet, or bar mills into the desired products.

Thus, from a study of the traceable history of wrought iron it is learned that many different processes of manufacture have been employed in its production. These different stages of development, each designed to improve quality and/or increase output, left unaltered the natural combination of high purity iron and siliceous slag which is found only in wrought iron.

Chapter V

THE INTRODUCTION OF OTHER
FERROUS METALS

I T HAS already been mentioned that cast iron was first produced during the fourteenth century and gradually came into use for many applications where ductility and relatively high strength were not required. This material differs greatly from wrought iron in chemical composition, physical properties, and structure. Some indication of this may be obtained by comparing the data in Chapter I with the chemical analysis and photomicrograph on Page 36.

Within recent years numerous changes have been made in foundry practice with a view to improving the properties of cast iron for special applications. Also, much work has been done along the line of alloy additions. Some of the alloys used include nickel, copper and chromium which are intended to increase strength or corrosion resistance or both. A typical analysis of one of the newer alloys is given as follows:

```
Total Carbon  ..........................................3.35 to 3.55%
Manganese  ..............................................0.60 to 0.80
Phosphorus  .............................................0.50 max.
Sulphur  ................................................0.125 max.
Silicon  ................................................2.25 to 2.50
Chromium  ...............................................0.50
Nickel  .................................................1.50
```

While the use of alloys has resulted in greater tensile strength and increased wear resistance, alloyed cast iron is not, however, greatly improved in ductility so, in this respect, it must remain in the broader classification of brittle materials. Little is known as yet about the influence of these alloys on the resistance of the metal to corrosion.

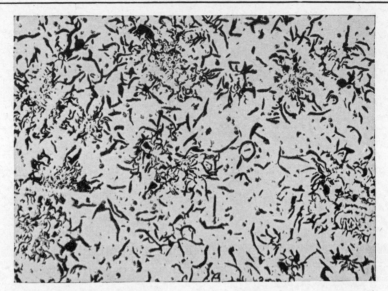

A photomicrograph and a typi-	Total Carbon	3.50 to 4.25%
cal chemical analysis of gray	Manganese	1.00 max.
cast iron. The dark areas are	Phosphorus	.25 to 1.00
flakes of graphite, or segregated	Sulphur	.125 max.
carbon particles.	Silicon	2.00 to 2.50

As a matter of historical interest, it should be mentioned that long before the introduction of the modern Bessemer and open-hearth steel making processes in the 1850's and 1860's, wrought iron was used as the raw material for making carbon steel by the cementation and crucible processes. There is every reason to believe that the cementation and crucible processes were known and used in ancient times but apparently they were lost to civilization during the dark ages. The Wootz steel of India and the famous sword blades of Damascus, Syria, and Toledo, Spain, were all made from wrought iron by the crucible process or a combination of that and the cementation process. About the year 1600 the cementation process was reintroduced in Belgium and in 1742 the crucible process was rediscovered in England. Both of these processes were used extensively during the eighteenth and nine-teenth centuries, and, of course, are still employed today but to a limited extent.

From the tonnage standpoint, the two most important modern

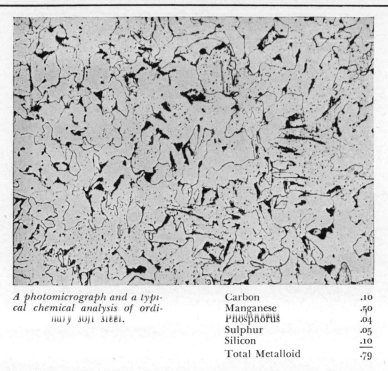

A photomicrograph and a typical chemical analysis of ordinary soft steel.	Carbon	.10
	Manganese	.50
	Phosphorus	.04
	Sulphur	.05
	Silicon	.10
	Total Metalloid	.79

processes for converting pig iron into a malleable product are the bessemer converter, invented in 1856 by Henry Bessemer, and the open-hearth furnace, invented in 1861 by William Siemens and successfully adapted to iron refining in 1868. Bessemer's development was intended to produce wrought iron of superior quality and at a lower cost than was possible by the hand-puddling process, but the product of his converter was steel, since it did not contain the siliceous slag which is always present in wrought iron. Outwardly, this new product looked like wrought iron, but had different physical characteristics. Also, there was promise of larger production and consequently lower price.

It was not until fifteen years after bessemer and open-hearth steel began to be used generally that much scientific attention was given to the corrosion-resisting qualities of this new metal. Then, in 1905, a group of American farmers appealed to the Department of Agriculture to investigate the cause of "fence wire corrosion."

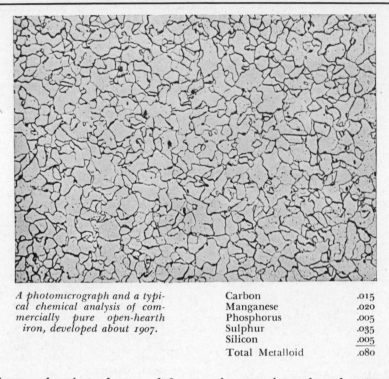

A photomicrograph and a typical chemical analysis of commercially pure open-hearth iron, developed about 1907.

Carbon	.015
Manganese	.020
Phosphorus	.005
Sulphur	.035
Silicon	.005
Total Metalloid	.080

Prior to the time that steel fence wire was introduced, wrought iron was used for the manufacture of wire. The conclusions resulting from the investigations carried on by the Department of Agriculture were in part, "The modern bessemer or open-hearth steel rusts more rapidly than iron wire, and manganese, especially if it is unevenly distributed in the steel, is at least in part the cause of the trouble."

These studies led to many modifications in steel practice and resulted in numerous attempts to overcome the lack of corrosion resistance. One eminent metallurgical authority, Colonel J. S. Trinham, in an address before the Birmingham Metallurgical Society, said:

"It has often occurred to me that the consuming desire of the steel maker is to make a steel which will last as long as wrought iron has already lasted. Imitation, it appears, is still the sincerest form of flattery."

A photomicrograph and a typical chemical analysis of copper-bearing steel developed about 1911.		
	Carbon	.10
	Manganese	.50
	Phosphorus	.04
	Sulphur	.05
	Silicon	.10
	Copper	.25
	Total Metalloid	1.04

Acting on the findings of the Department of Agriculture that the purity of wrought iron was responsible for its long life, commercially pure open-hearth iron was developed about 1907. This was the first of many subsequent attempts to emulate in ferrous metals the long life which has always characterized wrought iron.

Not satisfied that purity alone was responsible for the long life of wrought iron, another school of thought carried on an independent study and, having found traces of copper in some of the old samples, believed they could achieve their desire for longer life through the alloying of steel with copper. And so, about 1911, a fourth ferrous metal, copper-bearing steel, was announced.

Still another group, accepting neither the purity theory nor that supporting the addition of copper, believed that by combining both purity and copper the desired results would be achieved. Hence, about 1919 the fifth type of metal made its appearance.

39

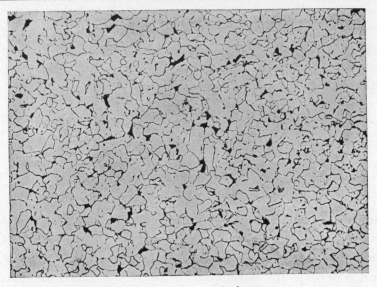

A photomicrograph and a chemical analysis of pipe made from copper-bearing, semi-refined open-hearth iron containing molybdenum. This metal was introduced about 1928.		
Carbon		.05
Manganese		.35
Phosphorus		.01
Sulphur		.02
Silicon		.02
Copper		.50
Molybdenum		.10
Total Metalloid		1.05

It was a copper-bearing, semi-refined, open-hearth iron having the following typical chemical composition:

Carbon	.030
Manganese	.120
Sulphur	.035
Phosphorus	.005
Silicon	.005
Copper	.240
Total Metalloid	.435

A sixth type of ferrous metal was introduced about 1928. It was essentially the same as its predecessor, except that the copper content was increased and a small quantity of molybdenum was added.

Within the past five or six years a new group of steels has appeared on the metallurgical horizon. This group includes the low-alloy high strength steels, many of which are claimed to possess both greater strength and greater corrosion resistance than the older steels and irons previously described. While these new steels vary considerably in chemical composition and physical properties, they all might be considered as generally similar. The following table of analyses includes several of the ones for which high resistance to corrosion is claimed.

	I	II	III	IV	V	VI
Carbon	.10 max.	.05 to .25	.12 max.	.12 max.	.12 max.	.14 max.
Manganese	.10 to .50	.30 to .90	.50 to 1.0	.50 to .70	.20 min.	.50 to 1.0
Phosphorus	.10 to .20	....	.10 max.	.10 to .15	.05 to .15	.04 to .12
Silicon	.50 to 1.0	.10 to .25	....	.30 max.	.10 max.	.05 to .50
Copper	.30 to .50	.85 to 1.1	.50 to 1.5	.90 to 1.25	.35 min.	.50 to .70
Nickel	....	1.5 to 2.0	.50 to 1.0	.45 to .65	.50 min.	.25 to .75
Chromium	.50 to 1.5	....	....	....	....	.20 to 1.0
Molybdenum	....	....	.10 min.	....	.05 min.	....

Analyses of other steels belonging to the same group could be listed but the ones shown should provide an indication of the attention being given to the problem of durability. Since corrosion is perhaps the most variable factor that confronts the user of metals it will be necessary to await the results obtained from the test of time before attempting to evaluate the many claims made for the superior corrosion resistance of these new steels.

Wrought iron, on the other hand, has remained unchanged in basic chemical and physical characteristics. It has been subjected to the most severe tests of time and has withstood them in such a manner as to assure its continued use for hundreds of services where durability is of primary importance. Consequently, in the following chapters the discussion centers on the quality requirements and characteristics of wrought iron and where the metal is finding its greatest fields of service.

Chapter VI

QUALITY STANDARDS FOR WROUGHT IRON

THE chemical composition, internal structural characteristics, and physical properties are the important features by which one may determine the quality of wrought iron or distinguish the material from other kinds of ferrous metals. These three features are discussed as follows:

CHEMICAL COMPOSITION

The commonly given analysis of wrought iron lists Carbon, Manganese, Phosphorus, Sulphur, and Silicon. However, since wrought iron is a two-component metal consisting of a high purity iron and iron silicate, and since the constituents are distributed between the metal and slag, it will be realized that the desirable analysis is one which discloses the distribution. Such an analysis is shown on page 3.

CARBON: The carbon content is usually lower in wrought iron than in steel, but it is not lower than in the class of open-hearth product known as ingot iron. Quality wrought iron is usually associated with a carbon content of 0.02% or 0.03%. However, in some cases good wrought iron may have a carbon content of 0.08% or 0.10%. Higher amounts may be an indication of imperfect or incomplete refining or may awaken a suspicion that steel scrap has been used in bushelling or piling.

MANGANESE: In well-made wrought iron, the manganese content is usually below 0.06%. High manganese may result from imperfect refining or it may indicate adulteration by the use of some steel in bushelling or piling.

The virtual absence of manganese in wrought iron and its almost universal presence in steel has resulted in the manganese determination being used as a means of identification and differentiation.

PHOSPHORUS: The phosphorus content of wrought iron is almost invariably higher than that of steel. It is in part alloyed with the base metal and in part associated with the slag. In well-made wrought iron the phosphorus content ordinarily ranges from 0.10% to 0.15%. In general, the lower range of phosphorus is advisable for products where high ductility is desirable, or where shock is a service factor.

SULPHUR: The element sulphur is not desirable in wrought iron, and, in conjunction with the low manganese content, is a promoter of hot shortness.

In certain classes of steel, sulphur is intentionally added to obtain better machinability, mainly through the formation and effects of manganese sulphide. This is not necessary in wrought iron because the ferrous silicate fibres confer a high degree of machinability, particularly in threading operations, without the aid of sulphur.

SILICON: The element silicon is quickly removed in the refining of iron. In wrought iron the usual silicon content is between 0.10% and 0.20%, practically all of which is in the siliceous slag component. (See analysis on page 3.)

STRUCTURAL CHARACTERISTICS

In view of the fact that wrought iron is a composite material, methods of examination which reveal the distribution of slag throughout the base metal, as well as the degree of refinement and homogeneity of base metal, are of paramount importance in identification and determination of quality. Such evidence may be visible to the naked eye through a macro-etch or may be apparent only through the use of the microscope.

Fracture Test

The nick bend, or fracture test, has long been a favorite way of quickly distinguishing wrought iron from steel. The former

43

exhibits a well-known fibrous fracture as contrasted with the crystalline break of the latter. At times there may be confusion, since dirty steel may show a semblance of fibre, while on other occasions good wrought iron may, if broken suddenly, exhibit some crystallinity which may be due to high carbon, high phosphorus or prolonged over-heating. Where the material is in question because of suspicion of scrap adulteration, a fracture test is of doubtful value and is liable to be misleading if it is the sole reliance for basing judgment.

Macroscopic Examination

Deep etching with acid is a prevalent inspection method in the selection of wrought iron products; particularly (1) as a means of disclosing methods of piling, and (2) for the detection of adulteration with steel scrap. Wrought iron etches deeply, with a roughened, stringy or woody surface, whereas steel will show a comparatively smooth surface. Consequently, a mixture of wrought iron with steel will exhibit a mixed type of surface if the distribution is sufficiently coarse to be discernible.

Microscopic Examination

The slag in wrought iron has a thread-like distribution in the metallic matrix; it is uniformly disseminated and there will be a few hundred thousand filaments per square inch in good wrought iron. The microscope has become the most useful adjunct in the study of wrought iron and in fixing quality standards.

The miscroscope will disclose:

1. Pearlitic areas due to carbon resulting from incomplete refinement in prevalent methods of manufacture of wrought iron, or from adulteration with steel scrap of even moderate carbon content.

2. Type of slag and its distribution; such as coarse slag pockets, fine textures resulting from heavy rolling reductions, or the absence of normal slag content.

44

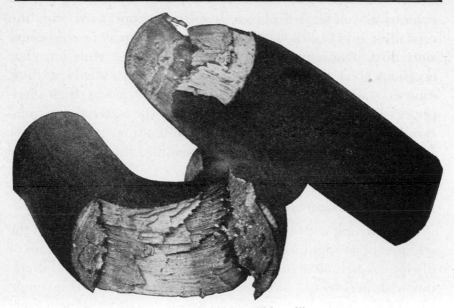

Wrought iron bars fractured to show the fibrous, hickory-like structure which is characteristic of the material.

3. Unusual characteristics of structure; such as coarsened grain caused by over-heating, high phosphorus "ghost lines" or other abnormalities.

In connection with any examination under the microscope it should be borne in mind that the area under observation is very small—pin-head in size at one hundred magnifications.

All of these test methods for determining the quality of the material are useful, but in applying them it is important that conclusions should be reached by weighing the evidence developed from the various ones employed. In determining the finer points of quality, experience in the interpretation of test results and a knowledge of the material's characteristics are essential.

In many instances it is impractical to conduct an elaborate series of tests and consequently in the majority of day-to-day purchases the problem of obtaining the desired quality of material has been greatly simplified through the development and use of good standardized specifications covering the various products. Because of its importance from the practical standpoint, the subject of material specifications is more fully covered further on in this discussion.

PHYSICAL PROPERTIES

The physical properties of wrought iron are largely those of pure iron. The strength, elasticity, and ductility are affected to some degree by small variations in the metalloid content and in even greater degree by the amount of the incorporated slag and the character of its distribution. Up to certain limits, ductility is increased by extra working, due to its effect in causing a finer distribution and more thread-like character of the incorporated slag. This is accomplished in modern practice through the large reduction of section obtained in rolling or forging large initial blooms into proportionately small final sections; or it may be obtained by rolling smaller initial masses to bar sections, which in turn are built into "piles," heated to welding temperature and rolled to desired forms. In common practice this is done once for "single-refined" wrought iron and twice for "double-refined" products.

Steel bars fractured to illustrate the crystalline or granular structure of the metal as contrasted with the fibrous structure of wrought iron.

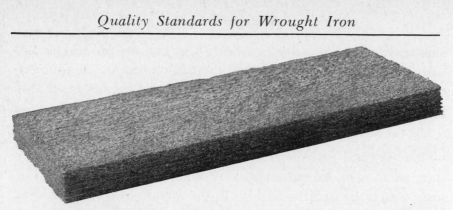

Wrought iron plate deep-etched in acid to bring out the fibrous structure.

The ultimate tensile strength and the ductility of wrought iron, unlike those properties of steel, are greater in the longitudinal or rolling direction than in the direction transverse to rolling. This difference is due to the nature of the slag distribution throughout the metal in the two directions.

However, within the past few years the development of rolling procedure has made possible an equalization of the normal ultimate strength and ductility in the two directions. This important advance in technique has had a marked influence in making possible the use of wrought iron plates for applications where severe fabrication requirements must be met. Current specifications of the American Society for Testing Materials covering Wrought Iron Plates—Designation A 42—recognize this development.

The value for the yield point of wrought iron is the same whether the material be tested in the longitudinal or transverse direction. The same statement also holds true in regard to the shear strength of the metal. The yield strength of the material as well as the shear strength are, of course, important factors in the design of structures for static loading.

The physical properties of wrought iron vary depending upon the type of finished product. The following list includes the physical test requirements of the commonly used American Society for Testing Materials specifications for several wrought iron products. In each case the product and designation number of the specification are indicated. The modifications in strengths

47

and elongations that are permissible for the various sections are not shown.

PIPE—A.S.T.M. Designation A 72

Tensile strength, min., lb. per sq. in.....................................40,000
Yield point, min., lb. per sq. in....................................24,000
Elongation in 8 in., min., percent....................................... 12

PLATES—A.S.T.M. Designation A 42

These minimum longitudinal requirements are for wrought iron plates produced by standard rolling operations:
Tensile strength, min., lb. per sq. in..................................48,000
Yield point, min., lb. per sq. in......................................27,000
Elongation in 8 in., min., percent..................................... 14

BARS, SINGLE AND DOUBLE REFINED—A.S.T.M. Designation A 189

	Bars Under 1⅝" in Diam. or Thickness	Bars 1⅝" to 2½" in Diam. or Thickness	Bars 2½" and Over in Diam. or Thickness and All Flat Bars
SINGLE REFINED BARS *			
Tensile strength, min., lb. per sq. in...	48,000	47,000	46,000
Yield point, min., lb. per sq. in........	0.60 T.S.	0.55 T.S.	0.50 T.S.
Elongation in 8 in., min., percent.......	25	22	20
Reduction of area, min., percent......	40	35	30
DOUBLE REFINED BARS			
Tensile strength, lb. per sq. in...	48 to 54,000	47 to 54,000	46 to 54,000
Yield point, min., lb. per sq. in........	0.60 T.S.	0.55 T.S.	0.50 T.S.
Elongation in 8 in., min., percent.......	28	25	22
Reduction of area, min., percent......	45	40	35

RIVETS—A.S.T.M. Designation A 152

Tensile strength, min., lb. per sq. in............................. 47,000
Yield point, min., lb. per sq. in.............................0.60 T.S.
Elongation in 8 in., min., percent: rounds ¼ to ⁷⁄₁₆ in. incl. in diam.......... 22
rounds over ⁷⁄₁₆ to ¾ in. incl. in diam...... 24
rounds over ¾ to 2 in. incl. in diam........ 28

STAYBOLTS, SOLID—A.S.T.M. Designation A 84

Tensile strength, lb. per sq. in. ....47 to 52,000
Yield point, min., lb. per sq. in.................................. 0.60 T.S.
Elongation in 8 in., min., percent................................. 30
Reduction of area, min., percent................................. 48

BLOOMS AND FORGINGS—A.S.T.M. Designation A 73

	Blooms	Forgings
Tensile strength, min., lb. per sq. in...............	45,000	45,000
Yield point, min., lb. per sq. in...................	0.50 T.S.	0.50 T.S.
Elongation in 4 in., min., percent....................	22	24
Reduction of area, min., percent...................	30	33

* Structural Shapes and Bars rolled direct from blooms are covered by A. S. T. M. designation A-207. Minimum properties of products covered by A-207 are the same as for single refined bars, A. S. T. M. designation A-189.

Other properties of wrought iron that are of value in engineering work are given as follows:

Weight per Cubic Foot...480 lbs.
Specific Gravity 7.70
Melting Point ....2750°F (approximately)
Coefficient of Lineal Expansion...................... .0000067302 in. per in.
per degree F
Specific Heat, room temperature..0.11
Thermal conductivity, K, (B.T.U. per hour,
per sq. ft., per in. of thickness, per degree
F difference in temperature)................................at 64°F—417.89
at 212°F—414.99
Electrical Resistivity—(at 21°C)..............................11.97 Microhms
per cm. per sq. cm.
Shear Strength (average)..............................38-40,000 lb. per sq. in.
Hardness:
    Brinell ....97 to 105
    Rockwell ....B_{55} to B60
Impact Strength—tested at 68°F
    Specimens machined from double refined wrought iron rounds
        Standard Charpy (Charpy test with keyhole notch)......24 to 28 ft. lbs.
        Standard Izod (Izod test with Izod V notch)............50 to 60 ft. lbs.
        Modified Charpy (Charpy test with Izod V notch)......70 to 85 ft. lbs.
    Longitudinal specimens machined from plate
        Modified Charpy (Charpy test with Izod V notch)......40 to 44 ft. lbs.
Magnetic Properties:
    Properties of a bar tested in "as rolled" condition were as follows:—
        Max. permeability, at B=8750 Gausses...........................1285
        Saturation Induction (at H=1500 Oersteds)
            B_s (Intrinsic) ....20,600 Gausses
            B (Total, or B_s+H)............................22,100 Gausses
        D. C. Hysteresis Data (Based on hysteresis loop having
        B_{MAX}=17,380 Gausses at H_{MAX}=100 Oersteds)
        Retentivity (Residual B).........................8,800 Gausses
        Coercive Force— (H_c) ....3.5 Oersteds
        Hysteresis loss—watt-seconds per cycle per pound of iron......0.1230
The same bar, tested after annealing for four hours at 850°C. and furnace
cooling had the following properties:—
        Max. permeability, occurring at B=8000 Gauses.................1870
        Saturation Induction (at H=1300 Oersteds)
            B_s (Intrinsic) ....20,500 Gausses
            B (Total, or B_s+H)............................21,800 Gausses
        D. C. Hysteresis Data— (Based on hysteresis loop having
        B_{MAX}=17,380 Gausses at H_{MAX}=100 Oersteds)
        Retentivity (Residual B).........................8000 Gausses
        Coercive Force ....2.23 Oersteds
        Hysteresis loss—watt-seconds per cycle per pound of iron......0.0934

A magnetization test (B-H curve data) was run on a similar bar, annealed at 900° C. Values were as follows:—

Amp—Turns per inch	Lines per sq. inch	H (Oersteds)	B (Gausses)
5	12000	2.48	1860
10	54000	4.95	8370
15	70000	7.42	10830
20	81000	9.90	12550
25	86000	12.4	13320
30	91000	14.9	14100
40	95000	19.8	14720
50	99000	24.8	15350

The curves on the opposite page, typical of the physical properties of wrought iron at temperatures between 400° and 1700° F., were plotted from results of tests on wrought iron pipe but, of course, wrought iron in other forms will show practically the same characteristics as there is no change in basic chemical composition from one product to another.

FUTURE POSSIBILITIES

Since scientific control is now possible, Byers Wrought Iron is uniformly high in quality. Blisters, once a common defect in even the best wrought iron pipe, are now practically unheard of. For many years, production of wrought iron plates was not commercially feasible. Now thousands of tons are produced annually. The bendability of wrought iron pipe has been improved, with the result that wrought iron coils bent to small radii are produced daily. Uniform, lower cost staybolt iron is available to railroads as a result of recent technical advances. These are only a few gains made possible by scientific control.

Further advances are constantly being made, and the alloy wrought iron field has intriguing possibilities. For example, large scale experimental work has revealed that the addition of $1\frac{1}{2}\%$ to 3% nickel markedly increases the strength of wrought iron. This is shown by the following table:

	Unalloyed Wrought Iron	3% Nickel Wrought Iron
Tensile Strength, p.s.i.	48,000	60,000
Yield Point, p.s.i.	30,000	45,000
Elongation in 8", percent	25	22
Reduction of Area, percent	45	40

These alloy wrought irons respond to heat treatment, and tests at sub-zero temperatures also show little reduction of impact strength. To the best of our knowledge, all other desirable properties are retained.

Studies, such as this, may lead to the production on a commercial scale of materials never before available which will combine the proven corrosion resistance and toughness of wrought iron with the greater physical strength of alloyed metals.

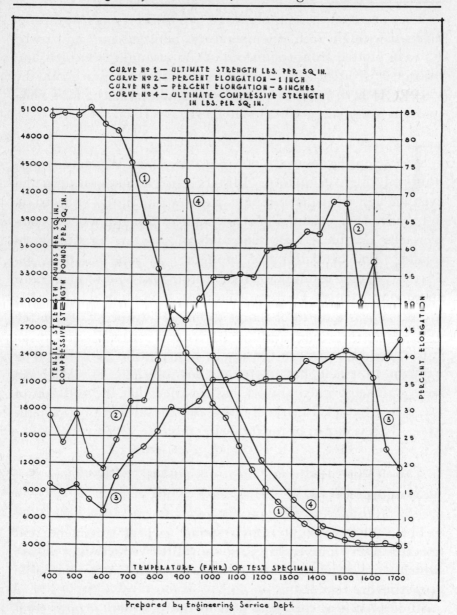

CURVE № 1 — ULTIMATE STRENGTH LBS. PER SQ. IN.
CURVE № 2 — PERCENT ELONGATION — 1 INCH
CURVE № 3 — PERCENT ELONGATION — 8 INCHES
CURVE № 4 — ULTIMATE COMPRESSIVE STRENGTH
IN LBS. PER SQ. IN.

TEMPERATURE (FAHR.) OF TEST SPECIMAN

Prepared by Engineering Service Dept.

Physical Properties of Wrought Iron at Elevated Temperatures

Chapter VII

SPECIFICATIONS AND DURABILITY TESTING

TODAY there is a constantly increasing number of new metals on the market, and the problem of differentiating between them is becoming a more difficult one for the specifier who does not have the time to keep abreast of developments. Since many of these newer metals are claimed to be very durable, particularly when subjected to corrosion, the problem of selection is further complicated. Obviously, the specifier must have a sound working knowledge of standard material specifications, because by using them he can save time and be assured of receiving the kind of material required. Also, he should be familiar with the limitations of accelerated and short-time durability tests since most of the claims for durability are founded on such tests. The following discussion is intended to clarify this situation from the standpoint of specifications and claims for wrought iron.

SPECIFYING WROUGHT IRON PRODUCTS

The leading technical organizations have developed and adopted a series of material standards which provide an excellent means of eliminating the problem of distinguishing clearly between wrought iron and other metals in preparing plans and specifications for any job. The use of these standards, many of which were developed only recently, makes it easy to prepare specifications that permit of no confusion, misunderstanding or misinterpretation as to the kind of metal required. It is always to the best interest of the owner, the specifying architect or engineer, and the contractor to avoid ambiguity in plans and specifications.

In the past, some of the terminology used in drawing up

specifications for wrought iron or steel products left room for reasonable doubt as to which of the two materials was desired. Specifications for piping installations were perhaps the most frequently misunderstood in this respect. For example, some of the terms that have been used erroneously to designate both Wrought Iron Pipe and Steel Pipe include—"Wrought Pipe," "Black Wrought Pipe," "Galvanized Wrought Pipe," "Iron Pipe," "Black Iron Pipe," "Galvanized Iron Pipe," "Black Pipe," "Galvanized Pipe," and "Genuine Wrought Pipe."

None of these terms is specific as to the kind of metal required and, therefore, should never be used when specifying or ordering either Wrought Iron Pipe or Steel Pipe. The word "WROUGHT" as applied to steel pipe resulted in so much confusion that many specifiers, who wanted to make sure of getting wrought iron pipe, adopted the term "Genuine Wrought Iron Pipe" which is widely employed today.

The terms "Black Pipe" and "Galvanized Pipe" are very confusing, and, unfortunately, have been used rather frequently. Neither term is correct without a qualification covering the kind of material required, because both wrought iron pipe and steel pipe are regularly furnished either black (uncoated) or galvanized (zinc coated).

Any term included in plans and specifications to designate a particular type of metal should be qualified and limited by certain definitions and requirements which eliminate the possibility of some other metal being substituted. Individually written material specifications may not cover all of the necessary definitions and requirements and for that reason alone it is highly desirable to employ recognized material standards.

The following list will provide a convenient reference for the most commonly used standards covering Wrought Iron Pipe and Flat Rolled Wrought Iron Products. When using any of these standards in drawing up plans and specifications, it is necessary only to refer to the number or title of the one under which the material is to be furnished and to the name of the organization that published it. For example, where it is desired to have wrought iron pipe furnished in accordance with the American Society for Testing Materials standard for that product, a paragraph such as the following should be included in the job specifications:

> "All wrought iron pipe specified in these specifications and on the accompanying drawings shall conform to the requirements of the latest revision of A.S.T.M. Designation A 72."

It will be noted that in the following list, the title and serial designation or number of each standard is given below the name of the technical organization or society by which it was adopted. Each of the standards is assigned a designation or number which does not change, and some of the organizations also include as a part of the number the date of issue or the date of the latest revision. For example, prior to 1939 the A.S.T.M. Standard for Welded Wrought Iron Pipe was known as A.S.T.M. Designation A 72-38, but due to a revision made in 1939, it is now known as A.S.T.M. Designation A 72-39. In making up this list, the date of issue, where used, has been omitted because it is subject to change.

American Society for Testing Materials

Welded Wrought Iron Pipe—A.S.T.M. Designation: A 72
Riveted Steel and Wrought Iron Pipe—A.S.T.M. Designation: A 138
Wrought Iron Plates—A.S.T.M. Designation: A 42
Uncoated Wrought Iron Sheets—A.S.T.M. Designation: A 162
Zinc-Coated (Galvanized) Wrought Iron Sheets—A.S.T.M. Designation: A 163
Rolled Wrought Iron Shapes and Bars—A.S.T.M. Designation: A 207
Single and Double Refined Wrought Iron Bars—A.S.T.M. Designation: A 189
Wrought Iron Rolled or Forged Blooms and Forgings—A.S.T.M. Designation: A 73
Wrought Iron Rivets and Rivet Rounds—A.S.T.M. Designation: A 152
Staybolt Wrought Iron, Solid—A.S.T.M. Designation: A 84
Staybolt Wrought Iron, Hollow Rolled—A.S.T.M. Designation: A 86
Iron and Steel Chain, A.S.T.M Designation: A 56

American Standards Association

> Welded Wrought Iron Pipe—A.S.A. No. B 36.2
> Riveted Steel and Wrought Iron Pipe—A.S.A. No. B 36.8
> Uncoated Wrought Iron Sheets—A.S.A. No. G 23
> Zinc-Coated (Galvanized) Wrought Iron Sheets—A.S.A. No. G 8.8

American Society of Mechanical Engineers

> Welded Wrought Iron Pipe—A.S.M.E. No. S-19
> Boiler, Rivet, Staybolt, and Extra-Refined Bar Iron—A.S.M.E. No. S-16

Association of American Railroads

> Welded Wrought Iron Pipe—A.A.R. Mechanical Division Specification M-306
> One-Inch Welded Wrought Iron Pipe—A.A.R. Signal Section Specification 129
> Refined Wrought Iron Bars—A.A.R. Mechanical Division Specification M-302
> Staybolt Iron, Hollow Rolled—A.A.R. Mechanical Division Specification M-304
> Staybolt Iron, Solid—A.A.R. Mechanical Division Specification M-305
> Iron and Steel Chain—A.A.R. Mechanical Division Specification M-301
> Wrought Iron Blooms and Forgings—A.A.R. Mechanical Division Specification M-307

American Petroleum Institute

> Line Pipe—A.P.I. Stds. No. 5-L
> Casing, Drill Pipe and Tubing—A.P.I. Stds. No. 5-A

Federal Specifications Board

> Pipe; Wrought Iron, Welded, Black and Galvanized—WW-P-441
> Iron Wrought (Refined): Bars—QQ-I-686
> Chain and Attachments; Standard, Miscellaneous—RR-C-271
> Ship Chain—RR-C-251
> Nipples, Pipe; Brass, Steel, and Wrought Iron—WW-N-351

U. S. Department of Commerce
Bureau of Marine Inspection and Navigation

Welded Wrought Iron Pipe—Rule I, Section 12, Fifty-first Supple
ment to General Rules and Regulations
Wrought Iron Bars for Stays and Staybolts—Rule I, Section 6, Fifty-
first Supplement to General Rules and Regulations
Rivet Iron—Rule I, Section 8, Fifty-first Supplement to General Rules
and Regulations

U. S. Department of Commerce, National Bureau of Standards

Pipe, Nipples; Brass, Copper, Steel, and Wrought Iron—Commercial
Standard CS 5

U. S. Navy Department

Pipe, Iron, Wrought—44 Pll
Iron, Wrought (Refined): Bars—46-I-7
Iron, Wrought; Plates, Black, 47-I-5
Chain and Attachments: Standard, Miscellaneous, 42-C-19 (Int.)

CORROSION AND FATIGUE TESTING

In addition to the chemical, physical and other tests made to
determine quality, various forms of short time tests have been
devised for proving the durability of metals intended for use in
services where corrosion and/or fatigue are encountered. Among
these several tests adopted by engineers for purposes of design
and for appraisal in relation to service conditions of employment,
it is quite generally admitted that corrosion testing is about the
most unsatisfactory in conforming to the ideals of selective tests.
In spite of a large amount of work done by standards associations
on this subject, there is as yet no general agreement or advocacy
of any tests as meeting the needs of the engineer for selection of
materials. Thus, data taken from installations operating under
normal conditions still provide the only reliable basis for proving
the durability of any metal.

However, tests have been employed extensively in attempting
to evaluate quickly the merits of newer metals on which reliable

data, taken from actual service, were not available. Many of these durability tests are of questionable value and since durability is a factor of such vital importance when metals are subjected to corrosion or fatigue conditions, a word of caution is justifiably offered against the unqualified acceptance of data from such tests.

CORROSION TESTING

The methods used to determine the corrosion resistance of metals fall into two general classifications, namely, service tests and accelerated tests. Properly conceived service tests, intelligently interpreted, provide a most useful guide, but in order to obtain reliable results they should be continued until the test specimens have failed. That, of course, requires time, and all too often conclusions based on the preliminary results are drawn.

The relatively large length of time required to secure results from service tests has favored the use of accelerated or laboratory tests. The use of data from accelerated tests was so vigorously advocated that it became necessary, in the interest of sound engineering, for various technical organizations and students of corrosion to investigate the reliability of such data.

To give a summary of such investigations would be beyond the scope of this volume; however, it may be considered indicative of the present day trend of engineering thought to remark that such authorities as The Institution of Civil Engineers of Great Britain, H. M. Boylston, Professor of Metallurgy of the Case School of Applied Science, and the American Society for Testing Materials have gone on record by stating that accelerated tests do not accurately forecast the life of metals in corrosive services.

The attitude of many towards accelerated corrosion tests is summed up in a pithy statement made in an editorial entitled, "Get-Rich-Quick Testing Methods," published in METALS AND ALLOYS for October, 1932:

> "On the whole, the short-cut methods are, like other get-rich-quick schemes, likely to be profitless in the end."

57

FATIGUE TESTING

The difficulty of duplicating actual service conditions in the laboratory is also encountered in fatigue testing. In order to obtain results quickly, it is necessary to alter the conditions by increasing both the stresses and the rate at which the reversals occur. An indication of the influence of differences between laboratory and actual service results is given by the following comments which appeared in a paper titled "Damage and Overstress in the Fatigue of Ferrous Materials," by H. W. Russell and W. A. Welcker, Jr., chief physicist and mechanical engineer, respectively, Battelle Memorial Institute, presented before the annual meeting of the American Society for Testing Materials in 1936:

> "After all the studies of failure under repeated stress and all the work it took to bring fatigue testing to the point where any laboratory will report the same endurance limit on standard-radius polished specimens of identical material, it is disconcerting to find that of two materials with different endurance limits, the one with the higher endurance limit is not necessarily the one which shows the best performance in actual service under repeated stress. For example, based on laboratory tests, wrought iron would scarcely be chosen for resistance to repeated stress, yet it is commonly used in railroad work for just such service, in spite of the laboratory evidence."

Where metals are subjected to either corrosion or fatigue or a combination of the two, many variables are involved and it is probable that for a long time to come the results of practical experience with metals in actual service will be given preference over laboratory results. This subject of laboratory testing was briefly but adequately summarized in the following words by the engineer of tests for one of our great railroad systems:

> "If my experience in comparing laboratory test results with service test results has taught me nothing else, it has taught me to beware of the danger that lies in too much dependence on the laboratory test. It is a valuable tool, but it may give very misleading results. This is especially true of attempts to test wrought iron and steel and measure the qualities of these two fundamentally different materials with the same laboratory yardstick."

Chapter VIII

THE CHARACTERISTICS OF WROUGHT IRON

A CLEAR understanding of the characteristics of wrought iron will enable specifiers to employ the metal more effectively in the solution of their problems involving the selection of materials to meet specific service conditions. From the standpoint of practical application and installation problems, the important characteristics of wrought iron include— resistance to corrosion, resistance to fatigue failure, the ability to take on and hold protective metallic and paint coatings, good machining and threading qualities and good forming and welding qualities. All of these, excepting the last two, are discussed in this chapter. Forming and Welding are discussed in the two following chapters.

RESISTANCE TO CORROSION

The principal virtues of wrought iron are its ability to resist corrosion and fatigue failure. Its corrosion-resistance is attributed to the purity of the iron base metal, freedom from segregated impurities, and the presence of the glass-like slag fibres embedded in the metal.

Corrosion is no respecter of metals. It is known that some metals are less susceptible to its effect than others, but there is no metal—precious, semi-precious or commercial—that is absolutely immune to all types of corrosion. Recognition of these facts will assist in the solution of corrosion problems.

The term "corrosion-resistance" as commonly applied is strictly relative and comparative. The only difference between any two metals from the standpoint of durability, when exposed to a given set of corrosive conditions, is that one will corrode more slowly and/or more uniformly, and, therefore, will last longer than the other.

Today most recognized authorities on corrosion agree that the film of corrosion products developed on a metal surface exposed to corroding media of various types has a pronounced influence on durability. The surface films developed on the commonly used ferrous metals can serve either to decrease or increase the rate of corrosion, and therefore may be classified into two groups according to the effect they produce. The first class includes films that are clearly visible and insoluble. Water will permeate them ordinarily, but they are sufficiently dense and adherent to blanket the underlying metal and thereby cause the corrosion rate to be retarded. Obviously, such films are desirable, and if broken will be replaced through natural processes.

The second class includes porous, non-adherent and non-uniform films which may accelerate corrosion. One of the most commonly observed effects of corrosion is the loose, porous scale which flakes off the surface of the metal at the slightest touch. Such films retain moisture. Where they are not uniform, the corroding solution is permitted to come in direct contact with the metal surface in certain areas, which, coupled with variations in oxygen concentration, creates concentration cells. The metal underlying the deposit and not freely supplied with oxygen becomes anodic to the metal lying on the fringe of the deposit where a plentiful supply of oxygen exists. Usually this results in pitting of the anodic metal beneath the rust film.

There are, of course, certain conditions to which metals must be subjected that are not conducive to the formation of films of either class. Probably the best example of this is found in handling solutions of some of the strong acids which develop no definite protective film or do not possess the power of Passivating the metal. Under this condition the surface is dissolved continuously, leaving bare metal exposed to further attack. Incidentally, it should be mentioned that accelerated laboratory corrosion tests of the acid type subject the metal to this condition.

Some metals have greater ability than others to develop natural protective films of corrosion products. That fact is primarily responsible for the difference in the corrosion resisting characteristics of the various metals.

It was about a decade or more ago that the corrosion-resistance of wrought iron was first attributed to protective film formation. Of course it had been recognized for quite some time that the slag fibres in wrought iron are present in such great numbers that they serve in one capacity as an effective mechanical barrier against the progress of corrosion, and, under most conditions, force it to spread over the surface of the metal rather than to pit or penetrate. Also, it was known that wrought iron had the ability to develop a dense, uniform and adherent skin or film of scale when exposed to the great majority of corrosive conditions, but this fact had never been taken into account in explaining its durability. Subsequent investigations revealed that the characteristics of this film, particularly its density and adherence, are influenced primarily by the siliceous slag fibres embedded in the iron base metal.

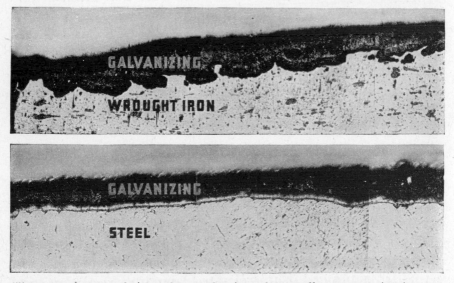

The reason that wrought iron takes on a heavier and more adherent protective zinc coating is illustrated clearly by these photomicrographs of galvanized wrought iron and galvanized steel pipe.

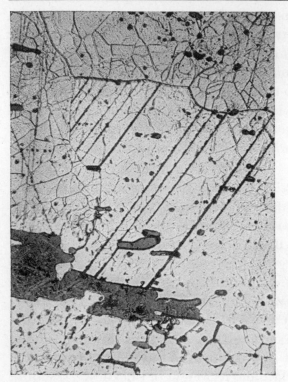

Photomicrograph of wrought iron which was in service for fifty years subjected to shock and vibration as well as corrosion. The parallel black lines represent the paths of slip planes which were intercepted by the slag fibres.

In some cases, the beneficial effect of the slag component is accentuated by the presence of compounds in the corroding medium that become occluded in the film and add to its effectiveness in protecting the underlying metal.

The record for durability that wrought iron has established over a long period of years, subjected to a wide variety of actual operating conditions, provides a sound engineering basis for its use in the many services for which it is specified today. Lacking imperishability in a metal, it is obviously safe and economical to employ one that has definitely proved its durability.

RESISTANCE TO FATIGUE FRACTURE

The ability of wrought iron to resist fatigue fracture explains the reason for the extensive use of this metal, particularly in the railroad and marine industries. Wrought iron is known to be relatively insensitive to notch effects and unusually resistant to over stress. These desirable properties are attributed primarily to high ductility and, of particular importance, to the presence of the slag fibres which confer on the metal a tough, fibrous structure somewhat analogous to that of a stranded wire cable. The slag fibres apparently serve to minimize stress concentration and deflect the path of slip planes that develop in a metal under the influence of conditions which ordinarily would result in fatigue failure.

Practical experience, over a long period of years, has shown that wrought iron will give much longer, useful life than other commonly used metals when subjected to conditions where sudden shock or constant vibration are encountered.

ADHERENCE AND WEIGHT OF PROTECTIVE COATINGS

Under some conditions where corrosion is a factor, the useful life of metals can be increased to some degree by the application of a protective coating, such as paint or galvanizing. The added life due to the coating will be influenced by the adherence of the coating to the metal surface and its weight or thickness. It should be remembered that the length of service life obtained from an installation subjected to corrosion will depend primarily on the durability of the metal itself, because after the coating is destroyed, the relatively thicker metal must bear the brunt of the corrosive attack.

It has been found through experience that either paint or hot-dipped metallic coatings, such as galvanizing, will adhere better and last longer on wrought iron than on the other commonly used metals. The answer lies in the fact that the natural surface of wrought iron is microscopically rougher than that of other metals and, therefore, provides a better "tooth," or anchorage for paints. In the case of galvanizing, the natural roughness of a wrought iron surface is accentuated by the acid pickling operation used to clean the metal before it is dipped in the molten zinc. The slag fibres are responsible for this increase in roughness.

Thus, a coat of zinc is given an even better anchorage than paint on wrought iron. As a result, wrought iron will take on a natural zinc coating which is 25% to 40% heavier than that on other metals and this makes the coating itself longer lived.

MACHINING AND THREADING PROPERTIES

The machinability or free cutting characteristics of wrought iron, like that of most other ferrous metals, is proportionable to its hardness which in turn can be compared with its tensile strength, since the latter two properties are comparable. However, in addition to hardness and tensile strength, there are certain structural features which may also have a pronounced influence on machinability. In the case of wrought iron, a very important feature is the presence of the siliceous slag fibres which are of distinct advantage, particularly in threading operations. In threading, the fibrous structure of the metal produces chips that crumble and clear the dies rather than ones that form long spirals. This of course promotes the production of clean, sharp threads on wrought iron pipe or other products that must be threaded.

Any properly adjusted hand-threading die or threading machine in good condition, furnished by a reputable manufacturer for threading ductile ferrous materials, will thread wrought iron with complete satisfaction. The minor variations in lip angle, lead and clearance are not sufficient to affect threading results.

A bulletin containing a detailed discussion of the threading of wrought iron pipe is available and may be obtained by writing to A. M. Byers Company.

Chapter IX

THE FORGING AND BENDING OF
WROUGHT IRON

SUCCESSFUL forming of any ductile metal depends to a large extent upon the fabricator's knowledge of the physical and internal structural characteristics of the metal, and the limitations imposed by the equipment available for use in carrying out the forming operations. Wrought iron products can be formed to meet practically any requirements using standard equipment. The forming may be done either hot or cold, depending upon the type and severity of the operation.

Since forging, pipe bending and plate bending are commonly used operations in the fabrication of wrought iron products, they are discussed in some detail in the following portion of this chapter.

FORGING WROUGHT IRON

Wrought iron is an easy material to forge using any of the common methods. The temperature at which the best results are obtained is somewhat higher than that used with soft steel because it is necessary to have the siliceous slag component in a softened or a plastic condition in order to make the material flow properly. Experience shows that a temperature in the range between 2100 to 2200 degrees F., corresponding to a bright yellow color, will give the best results. This is applicable to all types of forging work.

An important operation that may be broadly classed as forging is the forming of pipe laps for Van Stone joints. This type of joint is one of the strongest and most satisfactory joints that can be made in the installation of pipe. The Van Stone joint is

Forging Draw-bars for Locomotives from Wrought Iron Billets in the Shops of a Large Eastern Railroad.

made by butting together the flared or flanged ends of two lengths of pipe with a gasket between. These are held in place by collars on the ends of each of the lengths that are bolted together.

The principal operation in making a Van Stone joint is the flanging of the pipe ends. This operation can be performed on wrought iron using the same type of equipment as is used for steel. However, Van Stoning wrought iron must be done hot since it involves lateral excessive stretching of the metal to produce the radial flange. Furthermore, not only must the end of the pipe be heated to a forging temperature, but it must also be worked at that temperature. In flanging the smaller sizes, it is usually necessary to reheat the pipe end once or twice in order to complete the operation because the pipe loses heat very rapidly.

Under-heating or working at too low a temperature will usually be manifested by a splitting of the flange. This is commonly known as "sun flowering" and can be avoided easily by proper heating of the metal. In connection with the heating of wrought

Flanging Pipe to Make a Van Stone Joint

iron, preparatory to Van Stoning or other forging operations, it should be mentioned that there is very little possibility of burning the metal. With other metals there is a possibility of burning if the temperature is too high, but at the higher temperatures a slag flux forms on a wrought iron surface and serves to protect the metal against the danger of oxidation.

A more complete discussion of the Van Stoning of wrought iron pipe is found in our Service Bulletin, "The Bending and Flanging of Wrought Iron Pipe."

THE BENDING OF WROUGHT IRON PIPE

The corrosion and fatigue resisting properties of wrought iron have long been known and recognized by pipe users, but it is only within the past decade that exceptional bendability has been

67

developed in wrought iron pipe. Genuine Wrought Iron Bending Pipe permits short radius bends to be made successfully, either cold or hot, on a production schedule for the many applications where the corrosion and fatigue resistance of the material are so desirable.

Since pipe bending involves the working of metal, it is obvious that bending practice is of primary importance. Pipe bending is pipe stretching, and the amount of stretching that occurs in making a bend is affected by two factors: first, for a given size of pipe, the stretch *increases* as the diameter of bend is *decreased* and, second, for a bend of given diameter, the stretch *increases* as the pipe size is *increased*.

In actual bending practice, the metal on the inner radius of the bend is compressed slightly and this relieves the stretch in the outer wall somewhat. In addition, where no attempt is made to maintain the original diameter of the pipe in the bent zone, the outer wall flattens slightly.

In making a bend, the stretch in the metal has a tendency to localize at the central portion of the bend rather than to distribute itself uniformly. Therefore, successful results are obtained only by following a practice that will permit no portion of the bend to stretch beyond the safe limit

When bending pipe, either by hand or machine, it is desirable to conform to three main requirements:

1. The bending stress should be applied successively to short sections of the pipe.
2. The bent or stretched pipe should be advanced out of the bending zone and should not be subjected to further stress.
3. The force which does the bending should be applied as a steady pressure and not as a sharp blow or impact.

COLD BENDING

Properly designed machines ordinarily meet these requirements. Hand bending practice varies so widely that it is difficult to list a set of specific rules to follow. However, one very serious error, which may result in bend failures, is that the bend is started at the NEAR END instead of the FAR END of the length—thus:

WRONG METHOD

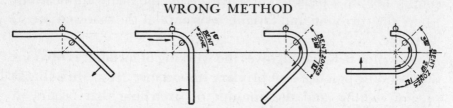

Note that the bent section is not advanced out of the bending zone; instead, it is subjected to additional stress and strain because it forms a part of the lever arm on which the force is exerted. This causes further stretching of the initially bent zones and may result in failure—either during the bending operations or after the pipe is in service.

With the right method, the bend is started at the FAR END of the length—thus:

RIGHT METHOD

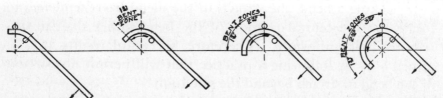

Note that the bent section is advanced out of the bending zone. It is not subjected to any further stress or strain, because it does not form part of the lever arm; the pipe used for leverage is at all times perfectly straight. Consequently, if the initial stretch in each zone is kept to a safe limit, the bend will not fail.

Where it is considered desirable to sand, or otherwise fill, pipe which is to be bent in order to preserve the bore diameter and prevent flattening of the outside of the pipe, the ratio of center-to-center diameter of bend to pipe diameter must be increased somewhat.

The following table shows the diameter to which each of several sizes of black wrought iron bending pipe can be bent as limited by both ductility and stiffness.

Wrought Iron

Minimum Diameter of Bends Which Can Be Made Cold
with Various Sizes of
Black Genuine Wrought Iron Bending Pipe

Size of Pipe	Minimum Diameter of Bend	
	Standard Weight	Extra Strong
3/8″	2.2″	2.2″
1/2	2.8	2.8
3/4	3.5	3.5
1	4.3	4.3
1 1/4	5.5	5.5
1 1/2	7.0	6.2
2	11.0	9.2

(Minimum diameters given are from center to center of pipe. Some degree of flattening is permitted.)

When cold bending wrought iron bending pipe in sizes 2½″ to 4″ inclusive, the minimum diameter of bend recommended is 10 times the nominal size of the pipe. These sizes and all larger sizes are usually bent hot.

It will be noted that this table applies only to black wrought iron bending pipe. It is possible to make closer bends with black than with galvanized pipe because the galvanizing operation decreases slightly the ductility of the material. This, of course, applies to all ferrous piping materials suitable for bending.

The cold bending of pipe sets up internal strains in the metal. These strains under many conditions of service are not of sufficient magnitude to affect the serviceability of the pipe. However, where pipe is bent to a close radius and where the service conditions subject it to vibratory stresses or expansion and contraction, it is highly desirable to relieve the internal strains if best results in service are to be secured. This can be accomplished economically by merely heating the bends to a dull red heat (about 1300°-1400° F.) and then allowing them to cool slowly. The practice of annealing pipe bends is becoming more prevalent and in some pipe fabricating shops it is regularly employed.

HOT BENDING

For certain classes of work, hot bending of pipe is desirable or necessary. With the smaller sizes, hot bending is usually accomplished without the use of sand filling to maintain the original bore diameter. Obviously, with this procedure, extreme care must be taken to avoid flattening and buckling of the pipe. The larger sizes of pipe are practically always sand-filled and generous diameters are usually allowed.

Since hot bending is more difficult to accomplish successfully than cold bending, it is necessary that the operator be thoroughly familiar with the following essentials:

1. Heating increases the ability of a metal to stretch and it is, therefore, easier to elongate it to the point of rupture.

2. There is a decided tendency in hot bending for the stretch to localize in the first thinned or elongated zone.

3. The greatest ductility in wrought iron is safely obtained at temperatures varying from 1300° to 1350° F. (this temperature range corresponds to a dark cherry red). Efforts to economize by heating pipe for bending with a torch have not produced the desired quality of bend as relatively small differences of temperature will tend to localize stretching in the hottest zones. Accordingly, furnaces specially designed for this work should be used as thorough soaking in the heating process and a uniform temperature over the whole bend zone is of prime importance.

4. The type of bending machine for hot bending is important. It should be of such a character that, as the pipe is progressively bent, subsequent pressure on the remainder of the pipe should be applied so that as little strain as possible will occur in the portion already bent.

5. Control of the stretch in a section already bent is usually gained by cooling with water before the following bend is made. In this operation, as in the others mentioned, the skill of an experienced operator is necessary.

The following table gives the minimum recommended hot bending diameters for various sizes of extra strong wrought iron bending pipe:

Minimum Diameters of Bends Recommended for Hot Bending
of Genuine Wrought Iron Bending Pipe

Size of Pipe	Minimum Dia. of Bend (Extra Strong)
½″	2.15″
¾	2.68
1	3.36
1¼	4.25
1½	4.86
2	6.08

(Minimum diameters are given from center to center of pipe)

The minimum diameter of bend recommended for hot bending wrought iron pipe in sizes 2½″ and larger is 8 times the nominal diameter of the pipe. The advisable bend diameter, especially for the larger sizes, is 10 times the nominal size of the pipe.

THE BENDING OF WROUGHT IRON PLATES

It was stated in one of the preceding chapters that wrought iron has directional properties, i.e., the ultimate tensile strength and the ductility are greater in the longitudinal or rolling direction than in the direction transverse to rolling. This characteristic of the metal is, of course, due to the presence of the slag fibres and, in plate bending operations, it has a direct influence on the limiting radius of bend in the two directions. In other words, the slag fibres in wrought iron affect its bendability in much the same manner that the grain affects the bendability of hickory wood. Therefore, it follows that a wrought iron plate can be bent to a shorter radius when the line or axis of bend is at right angles to the direction of the slag fibres than when the bend line is parallel to the fibre direction.

Since ductility is the most important property of the material from the standpoint of bendability, it should be mentioned that for standard wrought iron plates minimum ductility in the transverse direction is 2% in 8 in., while in the longitudinal direction the minimum ductility is 14% in 8 in. The relatively low transverse ductility of the material led to the development of special rolling procedures which made possible the production of wrought iron plates having much higher transverse ductilities than those produced by conventional rolling operations. This development is particularly important because it has made possible the use of wrought iron plates for many applications where the severe fabrication involved formerly prevented their use.

Since plate bending, like pipe bending, involves stretching of the metal, it follows then that if a plate is bent so as not to exceed the ductility of the metal, the amount of stretch that occurs on the outer surface of the bend will be dependent upon two factors, namely, (1) radius of bend, and, (2) thickness of plate. The effect of these two factors may be stated as follows:

1. For a given plate thickness, the percentage stretch per unit of length increases as the radius of bend decreases.
2. For a given radius of bend, the percentage of stretch per unit of length increases as the thickness of the plate increases.

In the latest revision of the American Society for Testing Materials Specification for Wrought Iron Plates, Designation A 42,

Wrought Iron Plates 3/4" Thick Being Formed in a Roll Bender for Fabrication into Large O.D. Pipe

73

provision is made for wrought iron plates having varying degrees of ductility in the transverse and longitudinal directions. The following table, taken from this specification, shows the minimum ductility requirements for the various classes of plates that are produced.

Minimum Ductility Requirement for
Wrought Iron Plates

Transverse Ductility (elongation in 8 in.) per cent	Minimum Longitudinal Properties	
	Tensile Strength, min., lb. per sq. in.	Elongation in 8 in., min., per cent
2	48 000*	14*
3	46 500	13
4	45 000	12
5	43 500	11
6	42 000	10
7	40 500	9
8	39 000	8

* Test requirements for the usual full longitudinal rolling of the plate.

From this table it can be seen that as the transverse ductility is increased until the minimum requirement is 8 per cent in 8 in., the ductility as well as tensile strength in the longitudinal direction decreases. Using these values as a basis, a formula has been derived for calculating the recommended radii to which wrought iron plates of various thicknesses can be bent in the two directions. This formula, which is given as follows, provides an ample factor of safety.

$$R = \frac{62\,T}{S} - .38\,T$$

Where R = Minimum radius of bend in inches
T = Thickness of plate in inches
S = Per cent elongation in eight inches

Using this formula and substituting the value for ductility that will come into play when the bend is made, the minimum radius of bend has been calculated for the several classes of plates in the various thicknesses. These values are given in the following table.

74

RECOMMENDED BENDING RADII FOR WROUGHT IRON PLATES

Plate thickness T (in Inches)	Value of S in per cent. 2	3	4	5	6	7	8	9	10	11	12	13	14
	Minimum Bending Radii in Inches—R												
3/16	5 3/4	3 13/16	2 13/16	2 1/4	1 7/8	1 9/16	1 3/8	1 1/4	1 1/16	1	1	13/16	3/4
1/4	7 5/8	5 1/16	3 3/4	3	2 1/2	2 3/16	1 13/16	1 5/8	1 7/16	1 5/16	1 3/16	1 1/8	1
5/16	9 9/16	6 5/16	4 3/4	3 3/4	3 1/8	2 5/8	2 5/16	2 1/16	1 13/16	1 5/8	1 1/2	1 3/8	1 1/4
3/8	11 1/2	7 5/8	5 11/16	4 1/2	3 3/4	3 3/16	2 3/4	2 7/16	2 3/16	2	1 13/16	1 5/8	1 1/2
7/16	13 1/4	8 7/8	6 5/8	5 1/4	4 3/8	3 11/16	3 1/4	2 7/8	2 9/16	2 5/16	2 1/8	1 15/16	1 3/4
1/2	15 5/16	10 1/8	7 9/16	6	5	4 1/4	3 11/16	3 1/4	2 13/16	2 5/8	2 3/8	2 3/16	2
5/8	19 1/8	12 11/16	9 7/16	7 1/2	6 1/4	5 5/16	4 5/8	4 1/16	3 5/8	3 5/16	3	2 3/4	2 9/16
3/4	22 15/16	15 3/16	11 5/16	9	7 7/16	6 3/8	5 1/2	4 7/8	4 3/8	3 15/16	3 9/16	3 5/16	3 1/16
7/8	26 13/16	17 3/4	13 1/4	10 1/2	8 11/16	7 7/16	6 7/16	5 11/16	5 1/16	4 5/8	4 3/16	3 13/16	3 9/16
1	30 5/8	20 5/16	15 1/8	12	9 15/16	8 1/2	7 3/8	6 1/2	5 13/16	5 1/4	4 13/16	4 3/8	4 1/16

Note 1—The radii given in this table were calculated to the nearest 1/16 in.

Note 2—These recommended bending radii are not to be taken as representing the absolute limit to which wrought iron plates can be bent. The values shown are sufficiently liberal to take into account ordinary variations in material, practice, and equipment.

The correct use of the table of "Recommended Bending Radii for Wrought Iron Plates" necessitates a thorough knowledge of the relation between the bend line or axis of bend and the direction of the fibre in the plate. For example, if a $\frac{1}{4}''$ standard rolled plate (minimum transverse ductility 2%, minimum longitudinal ductility 14%) is to be bent with the bend line parallel to the rolling direction, the recommended radius of bend will be $7\frac{5}{8}''$. If the bend is made with the bend line at right angles to the direction of rolling, the minimum radius of bend will be 1''. These values are obtained directly from the table by referring to the columns opposite $\frac{1}{4}''$ plate headed 2% and 14%.

However, there are conditions where a standard rolled plate with 2% transverse ductility and 14% longitudinal ductility cannot be used because the requirements demand a shorter radius bend than the $7\frac{5}{8}''$ given in the preceding example. For such conditions, it is obvious that the designer must select the type or class of plate that will bend to the desired radius. In other words, the plate must be specified in accordance with the ductility required to provide the necessary stretch that will occur when the bend is made.

While a majority of the plate bending is done cold, there are certain types of bends where it is desirable to work the metal hot. Naturally, any metal can be bent more easily when hot than when cold, and wrought iron is no exception.

As in cold bending, the radius of bend is a controlling factor in hot bending wrought iron plates. In general, the recommended bending radii shown in the table can be decreased by approximately 50% when hot bending is employed.

In hot bending, the temperature at which the metal is worked is a most important factor. Wrought iron plates should never be worked at a temperature in excess of 1,400° F. Best results will be obtained if the temperature is around 1,350° F. when the plate is bent.

At 1,350°-1,400° F. wrought iron plates will have a dull red color in the average lighted shop. It is always advisable to eye-gage the temperature after the plate has been placed in the die by looking underneath to see the color. This procedure will give a more nearly accurate idea as to the exact temperature.

If the temperature is to be measured with an optical pyrometer, every precaution should be taken to knock the scale off the surface of the metal before the reading is taken. If this is not done, an erroneous reading will ordinarily result, because the scale will be several hundred degrees cooler than the metal.

Space limitations do not permit the inclusion of complete discussions on the subjects of pipe bending and plate bending. However, separate publications giving complete information on each of these subjects are available and may be secured by writing A. M. Byers Company, Pittsburgh, Pa.

Spinning Machine for Forming Large Dished and Flanged Heads

77

Chapter X

THE WELDING OF WROUGHT IRON

WROUGHT iron can be welded easily by any of the commonly used processes, such as forge welding, electric resistance welding, electric metallic arc welding, electric carbon arc welding and gas or oxy-acetylene welding. The first two, of course, come under the classification of plastic welding, while the others are classed as fusion processes.

The absence of the A_1 point in wrought iron is of importance in reducing internal strains due to welding and in eliminating air-hardening capacity. However, internal strains cannot be eliminated as a factor and stress relieving of welded structures, particularly where heavy sections are involved, is considered good engineering practice today. Temperatures of 700°—800° F. are usually sufficient to relieve stresses induced through expansion and contraction by the heat of welding. Stress relieving is particularly desirable for equipment that is to be used in certain types of service, such as the handling of strong caustic solutions.

PLASTIC WELDING

When welding wrought iron by either the forge or the electric resistance methods, the important point to keep in mind is that the metal must be worked somewhat hotter than steel. In forge welding, for example, wrought iron is worked at what is termed a "sweating heat," which corresponds to a temperature of about 2500°-2550° F.

Plastic welding has been employed for many years with wrought iron. In fact, all standard wrought iron pipe and a majority of the large O.D. wrought iron pipe is produced by forge welding, which embraces both roll and hammer welding.

Resistance Welding Wrought Iron Pipe

Resistance welding has been employed in fabricating many wrought iron installations. When joining lengths of wrought iron pipe using resistance butt-welds, the best results are obtained by forcing the ends together with pressure that is just sufficient to produce a sound union. Excessive pressure usually results in pronounced upsetting action which may cause a reduction in the strength properties of the joint.

FUSION WELDING

The term fusion welding includes several different processes. The ones most commonly used in joining wrought iron sections are oxy-acetylene welding, electric metallic arc welding and electric carbon arc welding. Satisfactory results with any of these processes can be obtained only by following carefully the correct procedure. This, of course, is true regardless of the kind of metal to be welded. Furthermore, the exact procedure used with one kind of metal may not produce the best results if used with a different metal.

MANUAL OXY-ACETYLENE WELDING PROCEDURE

The procedure for welding wrought iron by the manual oxy-acetylene process is practically the same as that followed in welding soft steel of the same thickness. However, one important point to keep in mind is that the iron silicate or slag included in

Wrought Iron Ballast Deck Plates on a Railroad Bridge Being Welded by the Electric Metallic Arc Process

the metal melts at a temperature which is below the fusion point of the iron base metal. The melting of the slag gives the surface of the metal a greasy appearance. This should not be mistaken for actual fusion of the base metal; therefore, heating should be continued until the iron is fully melted.

The best oxy-acetylene welds are produced when perfect fusion is obtained without excessive mixing of the parent metal with the weld metal. Too much rubbing or agitation of the molten metal causes the formation of oxides which may be trapped in the weld. Ordinarily, just enough of the parent metal should be fused to provide a sound bond with the filler material.

The selection of welding rod metal is important. It is advisable to use a rod that has a yield point near that of wrought iron (27,000-30,000 lbs. per sq. in.) and to avoid rods containing high carbon or alloys solely intended to increase the strength properties. In general, any high quality low carbon rod should give entirely satisfactory results with wrought iron.

A neutral flame has been found to give the best results for gas welding wrought iron.

The first of the accompanying tables gives the essential details of the procedure to follow in manual oxy-acetylene welding of wrought iron. This procedure was found to produce welds of a quality to conform to the X-ray requirements of the A.S.M.E. Boiler Construction Code for Class I welds. However, other procedures may be employed that should produce welds that are just as satisfactory.

In establishing the procedure for gas welding wrought iron, it was found that for the thicker plates a step-by-step method of depositing beads produced the best results. For example, with 5/8″ thick plates the weld is started by depositing a root bead about 1½ inches long. A second bead is deposited on this and extended about 1½ inches beyond it, forming a new root bead. A third bead completes the weld for the first 1½ inches, forms a second bead for 1½ inches and a root bead for another inch and a half. The weld is completed by a continuation of this process.

Fabricating One of the All Welded Wrought Iron Trash Racks for the Tunnel Intake Structure at the Ft. Peck Dam, Montana

A layer method of depositing metal may also be selected for thick plates. Beads from $\frac{3}{16}''$ to $\frac{1}{4}''$ thick extending the entire length of the weld are used.

MANUAL METALLIC ARC WELDING PROCEDURE

In welding wrought iron by the electric metal arc process the best welds are produced when the welding speed is decreased slightly below that used for the same thickness of soft steel. This procedure is desirable because with reduced speed the pool of molten metal immediately following the arc is kept molten for a longer period of time, thus making for more complete elimination of the gases and affording the entrained slag an opportunity to float out of the weld metal.

Also, it may be necessary to employ a slightly lower current value than that used with the same thickness of mild steel, particularly in welding thin sections where there is a possibility of burning through the material.

Excessive penetration into the face of the parent metal should be avoided. The penetration should be no greater than that required to obtain a sound bond between the deposited metal and the parent metal, because fusion of an excess quantity of the parent metal tends to carry slag into the weld metal.

In metal arc welding, as in gas welding, the choice of filler metal is important. Any good quality low carbon rod either coated or bare can be used with wrought iron, but in general the coated rods are used more extensively in current installations.

One welding procedure found to produce very sound welds is given in Table II, "Manual Metal Arc Welding Procedure:" Other procedures may give equally satisfactory results. For certain classes of work where a greater degree of porosity may be permitted, larger electrodes, higher currents and higher speeds may be used.

Table II also gives the recommended rate of travel of the electrode in inches per minute that was found to produce good results. With manual operation it is practically impossible to maintain accurately a given speed, but the proper rate can be closely approximated by timing the actual rate of travel with a stop watch and then making any adjustments necessary.

In manual metal arc welding, as in gas welding, it was found that welds of a quality to conform to the X-ray requirements of the A.S.M.E. Boiler Construction Code for Class I welds can be made in wrought iron.

CARBON ARC WELDING PROCEDURE

The carbon arc process has been used with very satisfactory results in welding wrought iron. The procedure is the same as that used for soft steel except that arc voltages and amperages should be slightly lower than those recommended for soft steel.

FLAME CUTTING

In flame cutting of any ferrous metal, a neutral flame is first used to heat the metal to a temperature at which direct union with oxygen will occur. Then extra oxygen is supplied and the iron "burns" or oxidizes rapidly, with the evolution of heat.

In flame cutting steel, the gas pressure is usually about 10 pounds per sq. inch and the oxygen pressure is about 30 pounds per sq. inch. Due to the slag content of wrought iron, slight changes in procedure are necessary, and excellent results have been obtained with a gas pressure in the neighborhood of 5 pounds per sq. inch and an oxygen pressure of 15 pounds per sq. inch. Reduction of cutting speed is, of course, necessary when gas pressures are reduced.

With this procedure it is possible to develop a sufficiently smooth edge so that butt type fusion welds can be accomplished without subsequent trimming.

PHYSICAL PROPERTIES OF WELDS

Properly made welds in wrought iron will show ultimate tensile and yield strengths that are at least equal to, and usually greater than, those of the parent metal. While space does not permit the inclusion of specific data on the physical properties of welds in wrought iron, such data is available in a separate bulletin on the subject of welding that may be secured upon request to A. M. Byers Company. That bulletin contains the results of a comprehensive series of tests conducted by the American Bureau of Shipping, Lloyd's Register of Shipping, and the Bureau of Marine Inspection and Navigation, U. S. Department of Commerce, for the purpose of determining whether wrought iron plates could be welded to meet the requirements established by each of the organizations for metallic arc welds. The satisfactory results of the tests led each organization to approve the weldability of wrought iron to wrought iron and wrought iron to soft steel.

TABLE I—MANUAL OXY-ACETYLENE WELDING PROCEDURE

Thickness of Plate, inches....	1/8	1/4	3/8	1/2	5/8	3/4	7/8	1
Type of Joint	Single V	Single V	Single V	Single V	Single V	Single V	Single V	Single V
Angle (from perpendicular)..	30°	40°	40°	40°	40°	40°	40°	40°
Included Angle............	60°	80°	80°	80°	80°	80°	80°	80°
Spacing between Edges (starting end), inches	1/32	1/16	1/16	1/16	1/16	1/16	1/16	1/16
Spacing between Edges (18″ from starting end), in..	1/8	3/16	1/4	1/4	1/4	1/4	1/4	1/4
Diameter of Welding Rod— 1st Side, inches..........	1/8	3/16	1/4	1/4	1/4	1/4	1/4	1/4
Diameter of Welding Rod— Root Side*, inches........	1/8	3/16	3/16	3/16	3/16	1/4	1/4	1/4
Tip Sizes**	6	8	9	10	11	12	12	13
Oxygen Pressures**........	12	14	15	17	18	20	26	28
Number of Layers or Beads— 1st Side	1	1	1	2	3	3	4	5
Number of Layers or Beads— Root Side*	1	1	1	1	1	1	1	1

*When a double weld is required, as for example under the A.S.M.E. Code, Par. U-68, or U-69, a root bead is used.
** Tip sizes and oxygen pressures are for Oxweld welding blowpipe No. W17. The acetylene pressure may be any value from zero to 5 pounds. For other types of blowpipes use the tip size, oxygen and acetylene pressure recommended for steel of the same thickness.

TABLE II—MANUAL METAL ARC WELDING PROCEDURE

Thickness of Plate, inches....	1/4	3/8	1/2	5/8	3/4	7/8	1
Type of Joint	Single V	Single V	Single V	Single U	Single U	Double U	Double U
Angle (from perpendicular)..	30°	30°	30°	9°	9°	9°	9°
Included Angle............	60°	60°	60°	18°	18°	18°	18°
Radius, inches.............	None	None	None	1/4	1/4	1/4	1/4
Tongue, inches.............	0 to 1/16	0 to 1/16	0 to 1/16	3/32	3/32	3/32	3/32
Spacing between Edges, in...	5/32	5/32	5/32	None	None	None	None
Number of Passes..........	3	4	5	6	8	9	10
Diameter of Electrodes, in...	3/16	3/16	3/16	3/16	3/16	3/16	3/16
Amperes..................	170	170	180	180	180	180	180
Recommended Rate of Travel of Electrode in Inches per Minute							
1st Bead— 1st Side........	8	8	7	7	7	6	6
Intermediate Beads— 1st Side	5	5	5	5	5	5	5
Last Bead— 1st Side	5	5	4	4	4	4	4
1st Bead— 2nd Side	5*	5*	4*	4*	4*	6	6
Intermediate Beads—2nd Side						5	5
Last Bead—2nd Side........						4	4

*Not used unless a double weld is specified.

Chapter XI

THE PRINCIPAL APPLICATIONS
FOR WROUGHT IRON

TODAY, in the field of engineering construction and maintenance, wrought iron occupies a position that has increased rapidly in importance and wrought iron products are now employed for a greater number of applications than ever before. This is attributed partly to the fact that the economy of installing wrought iron has been established on the basis of results obtained in actual service and partly to the comparatively small increase in first or initial cost of a completed wrought iron installation over that of a similar installation in which the cheapest metal is used.

For almost a quarter of a century prior to 1930, pipe and oil country tubular material were the principal wrought iron prod-

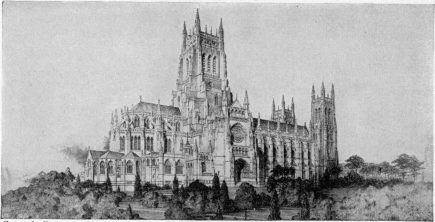

Cram & Ferguson, Architects

In the Cathedral of St. John the Divine, New York City, Built to "Endure for Centuries", Wrought Iron Was Installed in Piping Services where Durability Is Important. Wrought Iron in Various Forms Is Widely Used in Permanent Buildings of All Types.

86

Type S-1 Locomotive Built by the Pennsylvania Railroad Company and Exhibited at the 1939 New York World's Fair. This Ultra-Modern Locomotive, Designed for a Speed of 100 M.P.H., Has Time-Tested Wrought Iron Pipe in All Steam, Air, Water and Sand Delivery Lines.

Chicago Aerial Survey Company

Long-lived Metal Is Required for Many Purposes in the Construction of Public Works. An Excellent Example of This Is the North Side Sewage Disposal Plant in Chicago where Several Hundred Tons of Wrought Iron Pipe Are in Use.

The New Office Building for S. C. Johnson & Son, Inc., Designed by Frank Lloyd Wright.
Thousands of Feet of Wrought Iron Pipe Are Used in the Unusual Heating System
Which Consists of Steam Pipes Embedded in the Concrete Floor.

ucts with bars and forging stock competing for second place. However, within the past few years many wrought iron products have been added or reintroduced so that now the list includes—

Standard Weight Pipe
Extra Strong Pipe
Double Extra Strong Pipe
Reamed and Drifted Pipe
Railway Signal Pipe
Dry Kiln Pipe
Ammonia Pipe
Special Bending Pipe
O.D. Tubes for Unfired Heat Exchangers
Large O.D. Pipe
Line Pipe

Well Casing
Tubing
Drive Pipe
Couplings
Nipples
Cable Conduit
Well Drillers Pipe
Plates
Sheets
Angles
Channels
Rounds
Squares

Flats
Bevels
Half Rounds
Ovals
Half Ovals
Hexagons
Rerolling and Forging Billets
Flanged and Dished Tank Heads
Chain Iron
Staybolt Iron

Space limitations do not permit the inclusion of a detailed description of all the services in which wrought iron products are commonly used, but the following list will give an indication of the more prominent ones:

BUILDING CONSTRUCTION (including Residential, Religious, Educational, Hospital and Institutional, Public, Recreational, Commercial, Factory, Power Plant and Mill Buildings)
    Pipe: Cold and Hot Potable Water Lines; Soil, Waste, Vent and

Downspout Lines; Steam Supply and Condensate Return Lines in Heating, Power and Process Systems, Radiant Heating Coils; Air, Gas and Oil Lines; Boiler Feed and Blow-off Lines; Refrigeration Condensers; Cooling and Chilled Water Lines in Refrigeration and Air Conditioning Systems; Salt Water and Brine Lines; Refrigerant Lines; Heating and Cooling Coils; Process Lines including those conveying caustic soda, tallow, soap stock, paper stock, concentrated H_2SO_4, and raw water; Gasoline Lines; Skating Rink and Swimming Pool Piping; Well Piping; Fire Lines; Heat Exchangers; Underground Lines; Thermocouple Shields; Water Back Lines in Boiler Fire Boxes; Railings; Coal Chutes; Diesel Engine Exhaust Lines.

O. D. Tubes: Unfired Heat Exchangers for various services.

Plates, Sheets, Structurals and Bars: Cold and Hot Potable Water Tanks; Steam Condensate Tanks; Caustic Soda, Fuel Oil, Salt Water, Brine, Lubricating Oil, Beer, Yeast, Wort, Boiler Water and Miscellaneous Process Tanks; Trash Racks; Dust Collectors; Galvanizing Pots; Air Ducts; Smokestacks and Boiler Breechings; Coal Bunkers, Chutes and Conveyor Buckets; Refrigeration Condenser Pans; Cooling Tower Louvres; Roofing, Siding and Ventilators; Milk Can Washers; Gas Generator Shells; Electrical Relay Cabinet; Ornamental Iron Work; Bolts; Unfired Heat Exchanger Shells; Lintels.

The Grand Coulee Dam, O'Dair, Washington, under Construction. In Huge Projects Such as This Wrought Iron Is Used in Many Places Where Resistance to Corrosion or Fatigue Is Desired.

PUBLIC WORKS (including Locks, Dams, Water Treatment Plants, Sewers, Sewage Disposal Plants, Streets, Highways, Bridges, Canals, Harbors, Airports)

Pipe: Water Supply Lines and Conduits; Cold and Hot Water Lines; Drainage Lines; Air and Gas Lines; Steam Supply and Condensate Return Lines; Heating Coils in Sewage Sludge Tanks; Sludge Lines; Ocean Outfall Lines; Electrical Conduit; Dredge Pipe; Hand Railings; Weep Pipes; Underground Gasoline and Oil Lines; Sprinkler Lines; Water Well Casing; Large O. D. Sewer Lines.

Plates, Sheets, Structurals and Bars: Key Plates and Reinforcing Steel Protectors in Concrete Work; Gas Collection Hoods in Sewage Disposal Plants; Lock Valves; Weir Plates; Gratings; Trash Racks; Tie Rods; Roller and Lift Type Dam Gates; Lock Wall Protection Plates; Cover, Blast, Bearing, Fire Protection and Concrete Pier Protection Plates on Bridges; Storm Sewer Debris Buckets; Manhole Ladder Steps; Smokestacks; Hand Railings; Tanks.

TRANSPORTATION INDUSTRIES (including Railroad and Marine Applications)

Pipe: Air Brake, Steam, Water and Oil Lines on Locomotives and Cars; Cold and Hot Fresh and Salt Water Lines on Ships; Sanitary, Fire, Heating and Flushing Lines on Ships; Refrigeration Condensers and Brine Lines on Ships; Diesel Engine Exhaust Lines;

To Protect the Concrete Piers on Brooklyn's Huge New Marine Parkway Bridge from Disintegration in the Tidal Zone, Wrought Iron Pier Protection Plates Were Used Because of the Proved Resistance of This Metal to Salt Water Corrosion.

Railings, Fuel Oil Lines and Lubricating Oil Lines on Ships; Fire Lines on Piers; Bridge Railings and Floor Drains; Cargo Lines and Heating Coils on Oil Tankers.

Plates, Sheets, Structurals and Bars: Staybolts for Boilers; Coal Handling Equipment; Railroad Coaling Stations; Coal Cars; Smokestacks; Breechings; Smoke Jacks; Smoke and Air Ducts; Mufflers; Water Tanks, Oil and Gasoline Tanks; Roofing and Siding; Hull Plating; Deck Plating; Ventilators; Deck House Sheathing; Bulkheads; Rudders; Blast, Bearing, Cover, Brine Protection, Pier Protection and Deck Plates on Bridges; Brake Rods, Spring Hangers and Air Tanks on Cars and Locomotives; Superheater Bands; Drip Pans on Refrigerator Cars; Fire Screens on Piers; Structural Railings; Buoys; Lighthouse Structures; Docks and Piers; Track Watering Troughs for Locomotives; Gratings.

Forging Billets: Forgings for various services.

PETROLEUM INDUSTRY

Tubular Products: Oil Well Tubing and Casing; Heat Exchangers, Salt Water Disposal Lines; Oil and Gas Lines; Kerosene and Naphtha Lines, Rundown Lines; Sea Loading Lines; Refrigeration Condensers; Underground Pipe Lines.

In Ships' Piping Systems and for Many Other Marine Applications, Particularly Where Salt Water Is Encountered, Wrought Iron Has a Wide Field of Application.

Plates, Sheets and Structurals: Lease Tanks; Storage Tanks; Treating Tanks; Smokestacks and Breechings; Water Tanks; Roofing and Siding; Ventilators; Shoes for Floating Roof Tanks; Bolts and Nuts.

This listing is by no means complete, but it will provide an accurate indication of the various types of services for which wrought iron is being employed today.

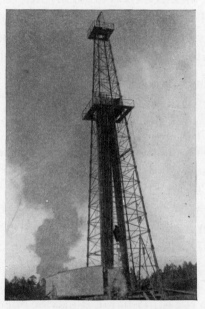

Running wrought iron tubing in a West Texas oil well. Resistance to corrosion and fatigue are important characteristics of metal employed in the oil industry.

Chapter XII

MATERIAL SELECTION

V OLUMES have been written on the subject of the durability of metals exposed to corrosive conditions and, undoubtedly, this is one of the most important subjects that confronts industry today. As pointed out in one of the previous chapters, there are many kinds of metal available but not one of them is immune to corrosion. True, some of them will corrode more slowly or more uniformly and, therefore, will last longer than others. For this reason, it is necessary to exercise the utmost care in selecting the metal for a specific application.

In the great majority of cases, economy is the criterion by which decisions are made regarding expenditures for new construction and maintenance work. Individuals charged with the responsibility of approving such expenditures fully realize the necessity of keeping these items within reasonable limits and, at the same time, of providing for installations that will give the ultimate of service life.

An economical installation may be one that has the lowest initial cost or, on the other hand, it may be one that has the lowest over-all cost per year of service. For those installations that come under the first classification it is customary to specify the cheapest material available; however when considering installations that fall into the second classification the problem of selecting the materials to be specified is of paramount importance. This fact is recognized by both executives and engineers since it has such a direct bearing on maintenance and repair charges.

The piping system in an industrial plant is an excellent example of one type of installation where it is desirable to maintain the cost per year of service at as low a figure as possible. In most plants the piping system has an important bearing on operating efficiency and maintenance charges. Failures in pipe lines may cause delays in production and frequently necessitate expensive replacements. When it is considered that the average plant piping system involves a great variety of services such as water lines, heating lines, power system piping, lines handling process solutions, gas and air lines, refrigeration system piping, and numerous others, and that in each of these services the pipe may be subjected to a different set of corrosive conditions, it is obvious that for the most economical installation the piping material specified must be selected on the basis of its over-all cost, rather than on the basis if its first or warehouse-floor cost.

With the wide variation in corrosive conditions normally found in actual service, it is obvious that no one metal can be expected to serve most economically and with the greatest degree of satisfaction, if used for all purposes. This has been definitely proved by actual experience and, therefore, it is necessary to select the metal that will withstand the operating conditions successfully. Intelligent selection of the proper material implies on the part of the engineer a thorough understanding of the corrosive conditions encountered and a good working knowledge of the relative durability of the metals available.

The services of our staff of experts are available without cost to anyone who is confronted with the problem of selecting the proper material to meet a specific set of operating conditions where ductile ferrous metals can be employed.

GLOSSARY OF TERMS RELATING TO WROUGHT IRON MANUFACTURE AND PRODUCTS

*WROUGHT IRON—A ferrous material, aggregated from a solidifying mass of pasty particles of highly refined metallic iron, with which, without subsequent fusion, is incorporated a minutely and uniformly distributed quantity of slag.

*BUSHELLING—The process of heating to a welding heat in a reverberatory furnace, miscellaneous iron, steel or a mixture of iron and steel scrap cut into small pieces.

*FAGOTING—The making of a "fagot" or "box," the bottom and sides of which are formed of muck or scrap bars and the interior of miscellaneous iron scrap or a mixture of iron and steel scrap.

*MUCK-BAR—Bar rolled from a squeezed bloom.

*COMMON IRON—Iron made from re-rolled scrap iron or a mixture of iron and steel scrap, no attempt being made to separate the iron and steel scrap.

*SLAB PILE—A pile built up wholly of flat bars of iron, all bars running the full length of the pile.

*BOX PILE—In manufacturing wrought iron bars, a pile, the outside of which is formed of flat bars and the interior of a number of small bars, all bars running the full length of the pile.

*REFINED BAR IRON OR REFINED WROUGHT IRON BARS— Iron bars rolled from a muck bar pile or from a box pile, of muck bars and wrought iron scrap bars free from steel, all bars running the full length of the pile.

*DOUBLE-REFINED IRON—Iron to be classed as double refined shall be all new wrought iron, which shall be first rolled into muck bars. These bars shall then be twice piled and re-rolled. All iron shall be free from steel and from foreign scrap. The manufacturer may use his own mill products of at least equal quality, but only in the first piling. In the final piling all bars shall be of the full length of the pile.

* These terms were taken from the standard definitions of terms relating to wrought iron specifications, A.S.T.M. Designation: A81-33.

FIBRE—The term "fibre" refers to the threads or fibres of iron silicate that are distributed uniformly throughout the high purity iron base metal in wrought iron.

FIBRE DIRECTION—The fibres of iron silicate or "slag" in wrought iron are produced during the rolling operations and extend in the direction of rolling. These fibres give the metal a distinct "grain" similar to that of hickory wood.

DUCTILITY—Ductility is the ability of a metal to stretch before rupture. This property of a metal is measured in terms of percentage elongation, i.e., the ratio of the amount of stretch to the original length of the specimen. When a test specimen is pulled to failure to determine the ductility, the maximum stretch occurs at the point of fracture, which is usually near the center, and the minimum occurs at the ends near the clamps. An 8-inch gage length is usually used in tests for determining the ductility of wrought iron.

TRANSVERSE DIRECTION—At right angles to the fibre direction or to the direction of rolling.

TRANSVERSE DUCTILITY—Ductility in the transverse direction.

LONGITUDINAL DIRECTION—Parallel to the fibre direction or to the direction of rolling.

LONGITUDINAL DUCTILITY—Ductility in the longitudinal direction.

STANDARD PLATES—Plates rolled in accordance with conventional procedure and possessing a minimum ductility of 2 per cent transversely and 14 per cent longitudinally. Standard plates are produced in three classes, namely, Standard Sheared Plates, Extra Long Sheared Plates and Universal Plates.

SPECIAL FORMING PLATES—Plates produced by special rolling procedures with minimum transverse ductilities ranging from 2 per cent to 8 per cent and minimum longitudinal ductilities ranging from 14 per cent to 8 per cent. This class of plates is intended for applications where difficult fabrication requirements must be met.

STANDARD PIPE—This classification includes three different weights of pipe commonly specified as Standard Weight Pipe, Extra Strong Pipe, and Double Extra Strong Pipe.

OIL COUNTRY TUBULAR MATERIAL—This classification includes Line Pipe, Tubing, Casing, Drive Pipe, and Drill Pipe.

LARGE O. D. PIPE—This term applies to all sizes of pipe larger than 12″ nominal size. The size is specified by stating the outside diameter in inches. In specifying this class of material, it is also necessary to state the wall thickness required.

LARGE I. D. PIPE—This term refers to the same class of material as O. D. Pipe except that the size is stated in terms of the inside diameter.

THREADS AND COUPLINGS—This term, ordinarily abbreviated "T&C," applies to pipe furnished with threads and couplings. Standard Weight Pipe is regularly furnished "T&C" while Extra Strong, Double Extra Strong, and the O. D. or I. D. sizes are furnished with plain ends, unless otherwise specified.

WELDING FITTINGS FOR PIPE—Fittings, including Bends, Sleeves, Nipples, Reducers, Van Stone Stub Ends and Caps, suitable for use in making welded installations.

GALVANIZING—This term refers to the coating of zinc applied to the surface of wrought iron or other ferrous metals by first cleaning and then dipping in a bath of molten zinc.

O. D. TUBES—Thin wall tubing, the size of which is stated by giving the outside diameter in inches and the wall thickness in Birmingham Wire Gauge numbers.